2004 POE

ONCE UPON
A RHYME

IMAGINATION FOR
A NEW GENERATION

Buckinghamshire
Edited by Steve Twelvetree

C000080741

 Young**Writers**

First published in Great Britain in 2004 by:
Young Writers
Remus House
Coltsfoot Drive
Peterborough
PE2 9JX
Telephone: 01733 890066
Website: www.youngwriters.co.uk

All Rights Reserved

© Copyright Contributors 2004

SB ISBN 1 84460 437 3

Foreword

Young Writers was established in 1991 and has been passionately devoted to the promotion of reading and writing in children and young adults ever since. The quest continues today. Young Writers remains as committed to engendering the fostering of burgeoning poetic and literary talent as ever.

This year's Young Writers competition has proven as vibrant and dynamic as ever and we are delighted to present a showcase of the best poetry from across the UK. Each poem has been carefully selected from a wealth of *Once Upon A Rhyme* entries before ultimately being published in this, our twelfth primary school poetry series.

Once again, we have been supremely impressed by the overall high quality of the entries we have received. The imagination, energy and creativity which has gone into each young writer's entry made choosing the best poems a challenging and often difficult but ultimately hugely rewarding task - the general high standard of the work submitted amply vindicating this opportunity to bring their poetry to a larger appreciative audience.

We sincerely hope you are pleased with our final selection and that you will enjoy *Once Upon A Rhyme Buckinghamshire* for many years to come.

Contents

Kalpani Perera (11)   16
Katie Durrant (7)   17
Nadia Rashid (9)   17
Sanya Parveen (11)   18
Connor Joynson (7)   18
Joshua Buckingham (10)   19
Bryony Perry (10)   19
Apple Cueto (9)   20
Emily Bryant (7)   20
Thaira Saleem (8)   20
Amina Sadiq (9)   21
Jay Horsler (8)   21
Giuseppina Martin (7)   21
Sabiya Khan (9)   22
Haajra Shahid (7)   22
Maisy Sharp (10)   23

Giffard Park Combined School
Rebecca Harrington (10)   23
Clare McNamee (10)   24
Helen Schmidt (9)   24
Alexander Barrie (9)   25
Julia Bloomfield (9)   25

Great Missenden CE Combined School
Dominic Janson (9)   26
Sam Barkaway (9)   26
Georgos Pantazis (8)   27
Macauley Hearn (8)   27
Jack McNeill (8)   28
William Dixon (8)   28
Hannah Dixon (8)   29
Jack Pounder (9)   29
Samuel Cook Gomme (8)   30
Robert Rose (8)   30
Imogen Foote (9)   31
Grace Varley (8)   31
Aisling O'Connor (9)   32
Lydia Anderson (9)   32
Anna Deacon (8)   33
Oliver Copping (9)   33

Luke Webb (8)	34
Francis Boyter (8)	34
Rosie Thomson (8)	35
Heather Burke (9)	35
Thomas Leakey (8)	36
Kate Howat (8)	36
Georgiana Macdonald (8)	37
Natasha Furmidge (9)	37
Charlotte Young (8)	38
Sophie Leese (8)	38
Alistair Hull (9)	39
Holly Broughton (8)	39
Danny McCree (8)	39
Jessica Sweeting (8)	40
Amy Walsh (9)	40
Fraser Scarlett (8)	40
Flora Stevenson (9)	41
Harriet Samuels (8)	41
Charlotte Wall (8)	41
Eloise Sear (8)	42
Meili Ellison (8)	42
Adriano Varriale (8)	43
Cameron Hurley (8)	43
Matthew Yeabsley (8)	44
Maddy North (8)	44
Thomas Burns (8)	45
Caitlin Batty (9)	45
Annabel Beard (8)	46
Leena Alyedreessy (8)	46
Zoë Candale (8)	46
Nick Wilson (8)	47
Sarah Hull (9)	47
George Cooke (8)	48
Hannah Cornish (8)	48
Kirsty Line (8)	48
Joshua Carty (8)	49
Jessica Gohl (9)	49
Betsy Seal (9)	49
Suzie McCarthy (9)	50
Andrea Loftus (9)	50
Harley Richardson (9)	51
Charlotte Debono (8)	51

Grendon Underwood School

Jack Elkington (10)	51
Helen Hewison (11)	52
Yannek Benson (10)	52
Garreth Bayliss (10)	53
Jacob Wilson (11)	53
Shaun Hunter (10)	54
Charlie Hobbs (9)	54
Tom Baker (10)	55
Rowan Wilson (9)	55
Emily Beebe (10)	56
Fiona Wilkins (10)	56
Charlie Carter (9)	57
Richard Crossley (10)	57
Joshua Boughton (10)	58
Jason Easton (11)	58
Emma Taylor (11)	59
Emma Hirst (10)	59
Jake Kenworthy (9)	60
Jamie Lipop (11)	60
Joseph Michael Cronshaw (11)	61
Joshua Fradley (10)	61
Connor Poole (10)	61
Rebecca Johnstone (10)	62
Amy Kimber (11)	62
Eleanor Martin (11)	63
Kelly Batchelor (11)	64
Nicolle Kniebe (11)	64
Danielle Brough (11)	65
Charlotte Fisher (11)	65
Chris McMahon (10)	66
Michael Goodwin (10)	66
Gracie Miller (11)	67
Marie Rawlings (10)	67
Barney Riley (11)	68
Ben Whitehead (11)	68
Ellie Clarke (11)	69
Connor Edwards-Bytom (9)	69
Jamie Rainsbury (10)	70
Mia Riley (9)	70
Jordan Petropoulos (9)	71
Max Brooks (9)	71

Laura Bell (9)	72
Keri Conway (9)	72
Mitchell Taylor (9)	73
Olivia Piontek (10)	73
Stuart Watts (10)	74
Adam Schofield (9)	74
Hayley Calow (11)	75
Ellie Culham (11)	75
Sophie Hawker (11)	75
Amber Wieland (8)	76
Heather Carlile (9)	76
Rhianna Yapp (9)	77
Jack Daly (10)	77
Melanie Beckerleg (11)	78
James Michael O'Rourke (9)	79
Hannah Darvas (8)	80
Owen Bevan (8)	80
Connor Day (8)	81
Kyle Carpenter (8)	81
Emma Owen (8)	82
Jamie White (9)	82
David Stow (9)	83
Sophie Dormer (9)	83
Bethan Topliss (10)	84
William Dukes (8)	84
Niamh Malewicz (8)	85
Rosie Lord (8)	85
Annie Lord (8)	85
Jessica Walters (8)	86
Jacob Brough (7)	86
Beth Gregory (9)	87
James Coomber (7)	87
Shannon Eustace (9)	88
Katie Lord	88
Adam Best (9)	89
Mathew Payne (9)	89
Zoe Malewicz (10)	90
Robert Lane (10)	90
Alex Black (9)	91
Isaac Elphick	91
Abigail Randall (9)	92
Sarah Ackroyd (9)	92

Emily Cudlipp (10)	93
George Howson	93
William Dearn (9)	94
Harriet Whitfield (7)	94
Jordan Garrad (8)	95
Tim Blackburn (9)	95
Ashleigh Doig (10)	96
Matthew Hawker (10)	97
Jack Boyden (9)	97
Rahul Patel (9)	98
Evangeline Martin (9)	98
David Payne (9)	99
Jack O'Donnell (9)	99
Eleanor Rosier (9)	100
Charlotte Farrow (10)	100
Alastair Bayne (10)	101
Natalie Tillman (11)	102
Olivia Barrett (9)	102
Peter King (11)	102
Hollie Miller (10)	103
Ryan Day (10)	103
Ryan James (11)	104
Rachael Hodges (10)	104
Alex Hirst (10)	104
Will Cook (11)	105
Rachael Sparkes (9)	105
Matthew Priestley (8)	106
Hannah Harris (8)	106
Shannon Ryan (10)	106
William Beckerleg (8)	107
Theresa Hurley (10)	107
Harry Protheroe (9)	108
Natasha Mason (8)	108
Olivia Pettengell (9)	109
Katie Thomas (10)	109
Zoë Ellison (8)	110
Amy Jay (8)	110
Ilana Brock (8)	110
Georgina Hearne (9)	111
Nathan Whitbread (8)	111
Luke Boasman (8)	111
Paige Hemming (8)	112

Ashley Thompson (8)   112
Kieran Kendrick (8)   112
Lucie Barnett (8)   113
Ben Saltzer (8)   113
Mats Venning (9)   114

Oak Green School

Jack Deering (10)   115
Sophie Sprowell (10)   115
Sheridan Richards (10)   116
Dale Scarlett (9)   116
Tania Illahi (10)   117
Laura Shoult (9)   117
Jemma Gates (11)   118
Haroon Humzah (9)   118
Ieva Pakalniskyte (8)   119
Nadia Hibat (9)   119
Maria Qaiser (8)   120
Rheanne Gordon (8)   120
Chelsea Davies (8)   121
Jody Collins (8)   121
Karina Price (8)   122
Hannah Baldwin (8)   122
Tayla Brown (8)   123
Michael Butler (8)   123
Amber Nasreen (8)   124
Lucy Warwick (8)   124
Fakhra Khalid (9)   125
Katie Rogers (10)   125
Clarice Farris (10)   126
Marty Jeffries (9)   126
Katy Warwick (10)   126

Oakley CE Combined School

George Turner (11)   127
Phillippa Needham (10)   128
Felicity North (10)   128
Samantha Powell (11)   129
Luke Young (10)   130
Jade Varney (11)   131
James Kilpin (9)   131

Taylor Soden (10)	154
Christian Alifoe (9)	154
Chloe Gibson (10)	155
Natalie Chan (11)	155
Kieran Clarke (11)	156
Danielle Klar (10)	156
Holly Matthew-John (10)	157
Meelie Clarke (10)	157
Michael Williams (11)	158
Chloe Osei-Bonsu (8)	158
Edward Finn (8)	159
Orlaith O'Hanlon (10)	160
James Barrett (10)	160
Anna Atkins (10)	161
Esther Adewuyi (9)	161
Cameron Lockhart (11)	162
Victoria Pickford (10)	162
Kate Hollins (8)	163
Hannah Smillie (8)	163
Connor Lauderdale (8)	164
Louise Crabbe	164
Joshua Gentry (9)	165
Ross Johnstone (9)	165
Elliot Moore (8)	165
Fraser Green (8)	166
Bethany Conway (7)	166
Olivia Hodgson (8)	166
James Cochrane (7)	167
Ryan Gray (10)	167
Sarah Gatley (8)	168
Joanna Lloyd-Knibbs (7)	168
Katy Worton (7)	168
Cameron Green (10)	169
Lisa-Maria Lamprecht (8)	169
Lucy Freeman (9)	169
Kirby Haddon (8)	170
Sophie Luckett (9)	170
Aine Lavelle (7)	170

Seer Green CE Combined School

Emily Smith (10)	171
Daniel Brennan (11)	171
Roisin McNeil (10)	172
Alex Damas (10)	173
James Howkins (11)	173
Catherine O'Brien (11)	174
Harry Evans (10)	174
Jessica Gamble (10)	175
Amy Quelch (11)	175
Sarah Popely (11)	176
Jennifer Rothwell (11)	177
Charlotte Pearce (10)	177
Daniella Camilleri (10)	178
Laura Babb (11)	179
Katrina Johnson (10)	180
Stephen Rosser (11)	181
Philip Grudier (11)	182
Alex Hayes (10)	182
Emma Campbell (10)	183
Edward Avery (10)	184
Jack Leeper (11)	184
Georgia Davis (10)	185
Amy Zelepuken-Smith (10)	186
Joe Clarke (11)	187

Stoke Mandeville Combined School

Andrew Granville (9)	187
Helena Walters (8)	188
Tyler Sear (9)	188
Georgina Hopkins (9)	189
Kate Bowman (8)	189
Louise Granville (9)	190
Farah Chaudhry (9)	190
Eleanor Simpson (8)	191
India Rowell (8)	191
Sophie Theodosiou (9)	192
Calum Grainge (9)	192
Rebecca Day (9)	193
William Dolder (9)	193
Dhaamin Clarke (8)	194

The Meadows Combined School

Matthew Chandler (8)	194
Zac Beckles (8)	195
Richard Nicoll (8)	195
James Sidebottom (8)	196
Joshua Davis (8)	196
Gemma Pryor (8)	196
Sian Kingsman (9)	197
Alice Walsh (8)	197
Matthew Jones (9)	197
Brandon Ricketts (8)	198
Hayley Carson (9)	198

Thorpe House School

Richard Logan (10)	199
Andrew Stephenson (10)	199
Jordan Moore (10)	200
Aidan Dean (10)	201
Oliver Levesley (10)	201
Alex Saunders (10)	202
William Airey (10)	202
Robert Coates (10)	203
George Barrett (10)	203
Neil Chandarana (10)	204
Samuel Hickman (10)	204
Harry Sapsford (11)	205
Thomas Parker (11)	205
Patrick Lock (11)	206
Olly Speed (10)	206
Ben Lucas-Lee (9)	207
Rowan Arkley (9)	207
Matthew Booth (9)	208
Ben Bridbury (9)	208
Niall Brogden (9)	209
Thomas Babb (10)	209
Jack Bingham (9)	210
Emilio Iannucci (10)	211
Ralph Higson (10)	212
Thomas Wait (9)	213
Ramir Sandhu (9)	214
James Wright (9)	215

William Harding Combined School

The Poems

The Writer Of This Poem

(Based on 'The Writer of this Poem' by Roger McGough)

The writer of this poem
Is as good as gold,
As hot as the sun,
And as powerful as God!

As strong as a brick,
More important than any queen,
As intelligent as 100 dolphins,
And as beautiful as a peacock.

The writer of this poem,
Is as smooth as ice,
Gives you tons of delights,
But that is fantasy.

Lucinda Black (9)

Haiku Fun

Deep under the sea
Sea snails will play hide-and-seek
Fishes blow bubbles.

Amy Lambourne (10)
Crown House School

Dreams Haiku

Dreams can be lovely,
Floating wherever you go,
Your own universe.

Chloe Butler (10)
Crown House School

Have You Ever?

Have you ever seen anything as wild
As a TV eating a child?

Have you ever looked at anything as bizarre
As an elephant driving a car?

Have you ever gasped at anything as weird
As a giraffe with a beard?

Have you ever witnessed anything as scary
As a tiger roaming the prairie?

Have you ever seen anything as uncanny
As a vampire for your nanny?

I have!

Ryan Gordon (10)
Crown House School

Just You And Me

As high as the moon,
As deep as the sea,
As far as the stars,
Just you and me.

I'll never forget you,
You'll never forget me,
Every day we were together,
Just you and me.

You are so special,
Honest and true,
We'll go on forever,
Just me and you.

Lucie Bradley (11)
Crown House School

How To Make A Cobbleswobble

All you have to do
To make a cobbleswobble
Is make a carrot stew
And add a kangaroo.

After you've done that,
Add a pink hat.
Plonk in a baboon,
Then stir with a balloon.

Your cobbleswobble's done,
Just give it a stir.
Be patient for a minute,
And you'll soon start growing fur!

Amrit Atwal (11)
Crown House School

Wonder

Have you ever wondered why:
Stars twinkle,
Birds fly,
Fingers wrinkle,
Cows moo,
Ducks swim,
Swans too,
Jelly wobbles,
Lions roar,
Dolphins squeak,
Adults get more?

Maria Khan (10)
Crown House School

The Best Rabbit In The World!

My rabbit's called Toffee,
His eyes are like coffee,
His paws are brown,
His knees bending down,
Up he jumps, spring, spring all round his little hutch.
I clean his hay almost every day,
If I give him food,
He's never in a mood.
Out he will trot,
When it is hot,
In he goes,
When it snows,
Snuggling safely in his hay.

Alisha Ahmed (8)
Crown House School

Wednesday

W e play in the playground
E nd of break we line up
D aniel is my best friend
N aughty Luke shouts out in class
E nd of day we have homework
S cience is fun
'D o not shout in class, Luke!' said Mr Kenyon
A t school we do spellings
Y esssssss, it's half term!

Alex Lau (8)
Crown House School

Death

What is death?
I never used to know,
Whenever I asked, everyone went quiet,
The pain came as a shock.

Five days,
Seven hours,
Thirty-six minutes ago,
He died.

The gravestone said he fell asleep,
But he's never woken since.
What is death?
I now know and I miss him so much.

Caitlin McKenna (11)
Crown House School

The Maths Lesson

Looking out of a window,
I see a lot of things,
Like buses, cars, building sites and people,
Even small clouds drifting by,
I see birds flying and gliding,
They land in trees which lose their leaves,
Then the teacher asks me an answer . . .
I don't know.

Ryan Gavin (10)
Crown House School

Death Haiku

Death is like burning
Fires in your heart. Like black holes
You fall deep down, down.

Sarah Weaver (10)
Crown House School

Rubbish Bin

A torn piece of paper
A bottle top
A plastic bottle
A dirty pear drop
Some stale bread
A rotten pear
Something your dog left on the stair
A broken pencil
A piece of glass
An unused door handle
Made of brass
An empty milk carton
An old broken boat
An old legless plastic goat
I looked in the bin
It really looked fun
Rubbish and litter from 100 to 1
But one thing made me stick my head down the well
This bin had a horrible smell.

Sarah Jones (8)
Crown House School

Cricket

I like to play cricket,
I like to bat,
Once I hit the ball in the air!
And it hit a cat.

Atiq Khan (8)
Crown House School

Where Do Teachers Keep Their Pets?

Mr Clark has a shark
Hiding in the park.

Mr Kenyan has a dog
In his dirty log.

Mrs England has a frog
That lives in her catalogue.

Mrs Brooks has a snail
That sleeps in her mail.

Mr Sorrell has a bat
Hiding in his sporty hat.

Mrs George has a mouse
That lives in the house.

Mrs Malliff has a croc
Living in her clock.

Mrs Child has a snake
Living in her Christmas cake.

Emma Weaver (8)
Crown House School

Snakes!

S nakes are cool
N ot fools!
A frican snakes are poisonous
K iller snakes are dangerous
E lephants squash snakes
S nakes don't eat cakes.

Jacob Fernandes (8)
Crown House School

Down In The Dumps There's . . .

Half a broken candle
A door handle
Made of brass
Here and there a few pieces of glass
A broken TV
And a dolly which once belonged to me
A snapped pen
The old remains of a toy hen
The leg of a chair
The rotten stalk of a mouldy pear
A box of unsticky stickers
A pair of ripped knickers
A very long tie
A broken plate that was used for an apple pie
A sofa with its springs sticking out
Pieces of cardboard here about
Oh, that stinky load
And it is going to gain more
Because our lot is going down the road.

Hattie Smith (8)
Crown House School

Pig With Wings!

F lying pigs are cool!
L ots of them are fat.
Y ou will see them drool!
I think they chase rats.
N one of them diet,
G ive way, they are flying off.

P igs like them start a riot!
I see them eat from a trough!
G ive them space to run.
S o they are really fun.

Jack Terry (9)
Crown House School

Friends

F riends are there for each other,
R oam the lands for another,
I need a friend till the very end,
E very person needs a friend,
N obody would not want any friends,
D o help somebody be a friend,
S ome people don't have a friend,
   so accompany them to the very end.

Kate Greenlee (8)
Crown House School

Alphabet

A is for apple round and crunchy,
L is for lamb soft and small,
P is for panda black and white,
H is for hand right and left,
A is for acorn round and hard,
B is for boat sailing out to sea,
E is for elephant grey and tough,
T is for teddy which you cuddle at night.

Laura Spencer (8)
Crown House School

Chocolate

C hocolate is so yummy,
H ot chocolate is my favourite drink,
O range flavour chocolate, it is OK,
C aramel and toffee are yummy,
L ight fluffy chocolate
A nd Maltesers are so scrummy,
T remendous chocolate melting in your mouth,
E legant chocolate is nice!

Georgia Hylton (9)
Crown House School

An Alphabet Of Toys

A is for Action Man, the hero of the world.
B is for Barbie, all the girls love.
C is for computers with the discs.
D is for digger, part of the demolition.
E is for elephant that squirts water.
F is for firemen that little ones like.
G is for Game Boy with a mixture of games.
H is for Harry Potter, the new wizard around.
I is for ice you chuck at people.
J is for jumping that makes you thin.
K is for Kai with Dranzer.
L is for Lego that you construct.
M is for Monopoly, the money game.
N is for Nintendo on the TV.
O is for Obelisk the tormentor.
P is for Play Mobile that you build.
Q is for Queens that are evil.
R is for robots that are deadly.
S for scooter that zooms along.
T is for trains on the track.
U is for unicorns that have horns.
V is for videos that I like to watch.
W is for Wombles that clean the mess.
X is for Xbox that is cool.
Y is for Yu-Gi-Oh, the playing cards.
Z is for zebras made from Lego.

Daniel Smallbone (8)
Crown House School

Where Teachers Keep Their Pets

Mrs England as a snake living in her chocolate cake,
Mr Kenyon has a bat living in his funny hat,
Mrs Brooks has a fish living in her china dish,
Mrs Malif has a kangaroo living in her smelly shoe,
And I keep my cat in my black rucksack

Harrisah Hussain (9)
Crown House School

Zac!

Don't pick up your hair, Zac!
Don't eat raw sausages, Zac!
Stop picking up people's coats, Zac!

Did you watch television again, Zac?
Did you tidy your bedroom, Zac?
I thought I told you to brush your teeth, Zac!

Don't run in the classroom, Zac!
Remember to push your chair in, Zac!
Will you play nicely, Zac!

Stop that clapping, Zac!
You're always singing, Zac!
Anyone would think I nagged you, Zac!

Zac Surman (8)
Elmhurst Junior School

James!

Don't talk about disasters, James!
Don't play fight, James!
Stop rushing your work, James!
Did you brush your teeth, James?
Did you make a mess, James?
I thought I told you to make your bed, James!
Don't be nasty, James!
Remember to get dressed, James!
Will you play with Marcus, James?
Stop that shouting, James!
Anyone would think I nagged you, James!

James Davis (8)
Elmhurst Junior School

Jack!

Don't run down the corridors, Jack!
Don't tell lies, Jack!
Stop that fighting, Jack!
Did you tidy your room, Jack?
Did you eat your dinner, Jack?
I thought I told you to brush your teeth, Jack!
Don't break your computer, Jack!
Remember your headache, Jack!
Will you stop moaning, Jack!
Stop that barking, Jack!
You're always talking about destroying things, Jack!
Anyone would think I nagged you, Jack!

Jack Rootes (7)
Elmhurst Junior School

Cats

My cats are beautiful
and witty
and sweet
and kind
and very good.
They can kiss you
but if you are not careful
they might bite.

Kirsty Grimstead (8)
Elmhurst Junior School

Space

Space is black,
With yellow dots,
They twinkle in the night,
With planets orbiting around them,
With the sun shining bright.

The sun is shining over the Earth,
With streaks of orange and yellow,
Sometimes it looks like it is smiling,
And I just wanted to say hello.

My favourite planet is Mars,
It is as red as an apple,
It is as hot as a fire,
But really it is as cold as ice.

Hannah Durrant (9)
Elmhurst Junior School

Love

Love is all around me,
Over and under.
Valentine's Day is all love.
Even in hard times,
Love still stands.

Leigh Duncombe (9)
Elmhurst Junior School

Florida

For the first time in my life
I entered the USA.
Eight whole hours I sat on that plane
But it felt like one whole day.

When we arrived I felt very small.
They checked our bags and let us go.
Me and my mum were soon in the mall
Dad and Jay stayed at the pool.

The theme parks were brill
And the rides fantastic,
110 percent pure skill.
103-110, the temperature was baking.

The food was amazing,
Too good for words.
The people were thoughtful,
I hope we go back soon!

Hannah Horsler (11)
Elmhurst Junior School

My Invisible Friend

My invisible friend likes pizza,
She eats my food all the time!
She is my very best friend you know,
But sometimes she's as sour as lime!

She whispers to me in class,
And we laugh and snigger together!
Everyone thinks I'm crazy,
They'll probably think that forever!

Charlotte Wilton (10)
Elmhurst Junior School

War

Country lads working on their farms,
Posters persuading the young boys to fight,
Parents sobbing, trying to make them stay,
Crowds cheering saying, ' This one is for England, lads.'
Trenches where people were shouting or calling for help.
The front line where they were sending more Tommies.
No-man's-land, barbed wire around the dead people's legs.
Flares seeing Fritz trying to run.
The soldiers setting off to fight.
Shells shooting the Germans until they give up.
Bayonets killing the innocent Tommy.
Poppies remembering those who have sacrificed their lives
for England.

Stefan Duncombe (11)
Elmhurst Junior School

Tonight's Night

Tonight's night is a starry night,
Where the wolves are howling to the moon.
Tonight's night is a romantic night,
Where the stars are shining into my room.
Tonight's night is a scary night,
Where the graveyard is extremely empty.
Tonight's night is a dreamy night,
Where my mind has extremely plenty.
But the night that I like best of all,
Is when snow is already at its fall!

Nadia Badshah (10)
Elmhurst Junior School

My Mum!

My mum has black hair
And she never is unfair.
I love my mum
And she loves me.
She is very sweet,
Because she gives me pocket money.
My mum is sweet,
My mum is a rose,
My mum is cool,
Because she has a pool.
My mum is super,
Because she can fix things.
That's why I love my mum.

Feryaal Shahid (10)
Elmhurst Junior School

There Was A Girl Called Lizzie

There was a girl called Lizzie
Who had a job that was so busy.
She had a beautiful dress
That got in a big mess,
Then she went to another city.

Gulsunam Bibi (11)
Elmhurst Junior School

War, War, War

Cold, confusing, crazy, war
Sad, scary, shocking, war
Mad, messy, miserable, war
Terrible, tragic, terrifying, war
War, war, war.

Kalpani Perera (11)
Elmhurst Junior School

Princesses

Princesses wear long and pretty gowns,
Princesses wear silky glass slippers,
They live in a castle or a palace,
And they like to eat posh meals.

Princesses wear golden tiaras,
And drink from a golden cup.
Princesses have a lot of golden things,
And have a lot of silver things.
They have soft, silky gloves.

They have long, soft, golden hair,
They put their hair up high,
They have a huge, comfortable bed,
With golden frills.

I like princesses,
Do you?

Katie Durrant (7)
Elmhurst Junior School

Space

In space there are lots of
Amazing things,
Things that we didn't know
Are there.
Like Saturn so bright and yellow
And Mars
So red it looks hot
But actually it is very cold.
And especially
The stars
That make space more special.

Nadia Rashid (9)
Elmhurst Junior School

Snow

Snow is falling
Laying a carpet everywhere
Unaware of the disturbance it will stir.

Children are playing
Making snowmen
Laughter is in the air!

Parents are moaning
Oh, it's so cold outside!
Fires are burning inside.

Cats and dogs are snoozing away
Unaware of what's going on outside
As long as the food is here
Who cares!

Sanya Parveen (11)
Elmhurst Junior School

Teachers

I love all my teachers
From my head down to my belly
I love to do my homework
Even though I miss my telly.

I love to do detention
I love to work real late
I polish all my teachers' shoes
I really think they're great.

And I'm very, very *mental!*

Connor Joynson (7)
Elmhurst Junior School

My Grandad

(January 1939-2003)

As funny as a clown,
A big heart of gold,
As happy as a puppy playing in a field.
Told jokes that could make you laugh like a hyena.
As sneaky as a spy,
As caring as a puppy's owner.
Worked like a mad man.
That was my grandad,
The best grandad in the world.
I miss him.

Joshua Buckingham (10)
Elmhurst Junior School

Winter

A blizzard was coming
A horrible humming
Through the trees
And ruffling leaves
Icy floors
And freezing doors
Frost on the windows
Cold things on the cotton wool
Not nice, not at all
Crispy ground
But wait, no sound.

Bryony Perry (10)
Elmhurst Junior School

Snowflakes Falling

S nowflakes falling
N ippy and shivering
O h, how crispy the snow is
W intry world
F rost is white, powdery ice
L ong, beautiful frost
A ll white
K ettle boiling for tea
E normous amount of snow.

Apple Cueto (9)
Elmhurst Junior School

Cats

Cats are furry
Cats are fun
Cats are good for everyone!
Why don't you go and see
Just how clever they can be!
In a pet store
In a cage
You can hardly tell their age!

Emily Bryant (7)
Elmhurst Junior School

Summer

Summer is the best,
Better than the rest.
You could have fun,
Playing in the sun.

Thaira Saleem (8)
Elmhurst Junior School

The Star And The Moon

The star above the moon,
The first star I see,
I make a wish,
You do it too.
The moon so bright in the sky,
With the star shining down on everyone.

Amina Sadiq (9)
Elmhurst Junior School

The Stance

There was a young man from France,
Who had an unusual stance,
Whenever he stands,
It's on both of his hands
And now it's become a new dance.

Jay Horsler (8)
Elmhurst Junior School

Cats

Cats are good
Cats are nice
Cats are beautiful.

Giuseppina Martin (7)
Elmhurst Junior School

School

I am writing a poem which is about my school,
We have playgrounds, fields and other things that are very cool.
We have pens and pencils, rubbers and sharpeners,
Which are our tools.

We go to school every day to learn,
But if we are naughty the teachers get concern
And if we work hard
Lots of merits we earn.

Books to our teachers is what we read,
A bigger library is what we need,
Knowledge to our brain
Is what we feed.

We run under the sun, just for fun,
If there is a race I want to be number one,
After a big day,
At 3.15 we are done.

Sabiya Khan (9)
Elmhurst Junior School

The Time Rhyme!

Once upon a time,
There was a little rhyme
And in that rhyme,
There sang a little chime
And in that chime,
We were late because
Of the *time!*

Haajra Shahid (7)
Elmhurst Junior School

Snow Is All Around

W indy, frosty weather
I cicles hanging
N asty and cold
T rying to keep warm
E xcellent snow
R ivers have turned to ice

S nowflakes falling
N othing but white
O h, what a delight
W onder winter.

Maisy Sharp (10)
Elmhurst Junior School

At School

At school I was good
good as can be
but boy, oh boy
was my sister bad.
She flushed Tim's shoe
down the loo
pulled Sue's hair
and stole her underwear.
I helped Tim fish his shoe
out the loo
fixed Sue's hair
and got back her underwear.

Rebecca Harrington (10)
Giffard Park Combined School

I Hate Spiders!

I always shiver when I stand near,
My teeth even chatter, just out of fear.
I bet just one bite would cause my fate,
This is why it's the thing I most hate!

With eight long legs covered with hair,
No wonder those spiders, give me a scare.
I would even faint with just one touch,
Those ugly spiders are just too much!

With enormous fangs,
From which poison hangs.
I hate them, those ugly things,
And the way my brother sings!

Clare McNamee (10)
Giffard Park Combined School

Snowing

S now all around, covering everything
N o sounds of birds, just shouting and laughing
O n it, the snow crunches under our feet
W hite blanket covers the windy trees
 I cicles hanging on the windows, like dragons' teeth,
                                    stuck in the wood
N ow a snowman being made, snowballs pattering
                                    as they are thrown
G etting wet and watching as the snow glitters.

Helen Schmidt (9)
Giffard Park Combined School

Ooga Booga

(Inspired by Walter De La Mare)

Ooga booga wooga woom,
here's a bride without a groom.
Bring a ring, bring a cake,
here's a cone without a flake.
Yum, yum, bring out the pie,
tooga tooga tooga tai,
look up in the sky, there is a buzzing fly.
Looga looga looga lee,
here's a cup without tea.
Shine, shine, wedding ring,
here's a bell without a ding.
Mooga mooga mooga muck
look there, it's just a book,
so go, go, go away,
and live to read another day.

Alexander Barrie (9)
Giffard Park Combined School

Night

Night, black as ink,
Though the stars appear to wink,
Night, is black.

Night, covers up the world,
From space it was hurled,
Night, is huge.

Night, from the universe,
It appears to have a curse,
Night, a robber.

Julia Bloomfield (9)
Giffard Park Combined School

The Monster

The monster is as brainless as an ancient bird's nest,
His hair is as crusty as old leaves,
His claws are as sharp as diamonds.

The monster's skin is like an old pair of underpants,
His eyes are like vicious lions,
His ears are like a snozzcumber,
He eats scumdiddlyumptious jelly.

The monster's breath smells like a maggot in a dustbin,
His teeth are like a scaly old hag,
His nose is like a bowl of spaghetti,
His feet are like razor blades.

The monster's head is like a peacock,
His hands are like thunder,
His neck is like honeysuckle,
He lives in a cave full of diamonds.

Dominic Janson (9)
Great Missenden CE Combined School

Christmas Is . . .

Snow flying gently
Angels singing sweetly
Food being crunched
Snowman made greatly
And Santa shouting,
'Ho, ho, ho!'

Sam Barkaway (9)
Great Missenden CE Combined School

Christmas Tree

Around my Christmas tree I hope to find:
One chewy chocolate,
Two sparkling snowmen,
Three special cards,
Four bouncy, bright globes,
Five munchy, crunchy candies,
Six crackling candles,
Seven rocking reindeer,
Eight furry teddy bears,
Nine glistening stars,
Ten silly robins,
Eleven tasty puddings,
Twelve golden holly bushes,
And one blessed baby,
That's what I would like to see,
Around my Christmas tree.

Georgos Pantazis (8)
Great Missenden CE Combined School

Christmas Acrostic

C rackers are banging madly
H olly is prickling wildly
R obins are flying madly
I cing scattering everywhere
S now falling everywhere
T urkeys are cooking
M ince pies are being eaten
A pples floating
S ledges slide madly.

Macauley Hearn (8)
Great Missenden CE Combined School

Modern Carol

On the 12th day of Christmas my true love gave to me:

12 sports cars a-racing,
11 CDs a-playing,
10 bagpipes a-piping,
9 trombones a-beeping,
8 children a-working,
7 guinea pigs a-nibbling,
6 dogs a-barking,
5 PlayStation games a-playing
4 singing ducks a-quacking,
3 Scottish osprey a-flying,
2 sea turtles a-swimming,
And a Canadian a-snowboarding!

Jack McNeill (8)
Great Missenden CE Combined School

What Am I?

It's as long as a twig,
As stripy as a zebra,
As fast as a cheetah,
It flies like a Frisbee,
It flies over the water.
What am I?

Answer: A dragonfly.

William Dixon (8)
Great Missenden CE Combined School

The Monster

The man that I know has hair like a dragon,
The man that I know has a face like a witch,
The man that I know has a chin like a wizard.

The man that I know has arms like a frog,
The man that I know has shoulders like a lion,
The man that I know has a tummy like a cow.

The man that I know has hips like a pony,
The man that I know has knees like a camel,
The man that I know has heels like an elephant.

The man that I know is a complete . . .
Monster!

Hannah Dixon (8)
Great Missenden CE Combined School

What Am I?

I am as long as a plank of wood,
I have black lines on me,
I have numbers on me,
I help you in your work.
What am I?

Answer: A ruler.

Jack Pounder (9)
Great Missenden CE Combined School

The Writer Of This Poem . . .

(Based on 'The Writer of this Poem' by Roger McGough)

Is as tall as a skyscraper
As strong as a mountain
As gentle as a leaf
As fast as a rhino
As slow as a hedgehog
As happy as me
As silly as a clown
As tall as a mountain
As clever as a monkey
As lovely as a flower
As cool as a cool dude.

Samuel Cook Gomme (8)
Great Missenden CE Combined School

Chocolates

C hocolate is so nice
H owever it is served
O h, how I love it so much
C hocolate is my dream
O range or mint
L ots of it is good
A nything will do
T omorrow I will
E at them all!
S o watch out chocolate bars!

Robert Rose (8)
Great Missenden CE Combined School

I Saw Someone With . . .

Teeth as vicious as an evil tiger,
Ears as sneaky as a rat,
Nose as pointed as a sword blade,
Chest as hairy as a lion's mane,
Armpits as smelly as a fish,
Arms as round as a sausage,
Bottom as spotty as a leopard,
Tummy as fat as an elephant,
Feet as smelly as gone off cheese,
Toes as plump as a potato,
Brain as small as a pea,
Head as round as a golf ball,
Beard as long as a tree,
Cheeks as droopy as a hanging apple.

Imogen Foote (9)
Great Missenden CE Combined School

What Is Colour?

I asked the boy who could not see,
'What is colour like?'
And this is what he told to me:
Gold is like a freshly baked cake,
Green is like a fresh blanket of spring grass,
Pink is a beautiful rose queen,
Red is an extraordinarily loud drum,
Yellow is a glowing ring above a spirit,
Black is a deep, dark hole that never ends
And purple is an angel drifting down from cloud nine.

Grace Varley (8)
Great Missenden CE Combined School

After School Clubs

On Monday I go swimming,
It's really fun and helpful,
But very exhausting.

On Tuesday I do ballet,
It's really fun, helpful and graceful,
But very tiring.

On Wednesday I do drama,
It's really fun and dramatic,
But very energetic.

On Thursday I do gym,
It's really fun, helpful and graceful,
But a little weary.

On Friday I do nothing,
But watch TV,
And I am carefree.

Aisling O'Connor (9)
Great Missenden CE Combined School

I Asked A Little Girl Who Could Not See!

I asked a little girl who could not see,
'And what is colour like?'
'Well um, bronze is just like leaves falling off trees in the
autumn time,
Orange is like a warm fire warming you up from head to toe,
Black is like a nightmare which we won't wake up from for
hours and hours,
Grey is like evil heading for you,
And I think gold is like a star twinkling way up high in the sky!'

Lydia Anderson (9)
Great Missenden CE Combined School

The Writer Of This Poem

(Based on 'The Writer of this Poem' by Roger McGough)

The writer of this poem,
Is as smooth as washed hair,
As smart as a sheep dog,
Neater than neat.

Never nosy,
As clean as bathwater,
Powerful as lightning,
Generous as ever.

As fast as a shark,
As strong as a kidnapper,
As helpful as Anna Deacon,
As marvellous as dogs.

The writer of this poem,
Never ceases to amaze,
She's one in a million,
Or so the poem says.

Anna Deacon (8)
Great Missenden CE Combined School

Mysterious Parcel

What's inside?
Golden snowflakes drifting
or a snowman coming to life?
A Christmas pudding filled with happy delights
or Rudolph with his red nose?
Maybe snow that never snows
or an elf that's 10 metres tall
or a polar bear who is half a metre small?
I feel it. I open it.
I turn it upside down.
I can't wait.
Yes!

Oliver Copping (9)
Great Missenden CE Combined School

My Christmas Desire

I wonder what's inside the Christmas present?
Is it Rudolph with his gleaming red nose,
Or is it Winter Wonderland where it always snows?

It might be snow that always will fall,
Or is it Santa climbing up our wall?

Is it Frosty the Snowman that will come to life,
Or is it Santa's very lovely wife?

There's only one day until Christmas Day,
I hope when Santa comes he will like to stay.

Luke Webb (8)
Great Missenden CE Combined School

What Is Colour?

I asked a boy who could not see, 'What is colour like?'
And this is what he told me:
White is a sheet of cloth without a crease,
Purple is the shade of a cloud,
Green is the thick carpet over the spring farm field,
Red is the crown of a rose,
Silver is the reflection of a knight's armour on the moon,
Brown is the smell of hot chocolate,
Gold is the smell of treasure.
    That is what colour is.

Francis Boyter (8)
Great Missenden CE Combined School

That's What I Want For Christmas

Misty angels swooping overhead in the starry sky,
That's what I want for Christmas.

A silver snowflake twirling and whirling,
Surrounded by clumps of twinkling icicles,
That's what I want for Christmas.

A shining, red-nosed reindeer,
Prancing as it swiftly disappears in the snow,
That's what I want for Christmas.

A jolly old man with a beard going, 'Ho, ho, ho,'
Filling the stocking by the crackling fire,
That's what I want for Christmas.

A snowman dancing around the yard,
With a soft, red scarf and a fluffy hat waving in the wind,
That's what I want for Christmas.

It's Christmas Eve,
Hurry up and get in bed,
Santa please, I've gone to sleep,
Sweet dreams drifting in my head.

Rosie Thomson (8)
Great Missenden CE Combined School

What Is Colour?

I asked the boy who cannot see,
'What is colour like?'
And this is what he told me:

'Blue is the fresh summer's sky,
Green is the fresh spring grass,
Red is the blood of a cut knee,
White is as pure as fresh winter's snow,
Gold is the bright sun shining in the sky,
Silver is the brightly coloured star,
Black is as terrifying as a dream,
Purple is a fairy drifting through the summer air.'

Heather Burke (9)
Great Missenden CE Combined School

What Is Colour?

I asked the boy who cannot see,
'What is colour like?'
And this is what he told me:
Black is like a dream that's dreadful,
White is like frozen ice on a winter's day,
Orange is the blazing sun at evening,
Green is the crispy leaves in autumn,
Purple is a fresh smell of roses,
Red is the love of Valentines,
Gold is the bright gleaming sun at midday,
Yellow is the crackling of the fire,
That is what colour is.

Thomas Leakey (8)
Great Missenden CE Combined School

Warning! Deadly Black Widow Spider!

Jet-black
Wearing a red spotted mac.

Hardly sleeps,
Always creeps.

Kills insects with a venomous bite,
Always hunts in the middle of the night.

Travels at a very high speed,
Camouflage? No need!

Kate Howat (8)
Great Missenden CE Combined School

What's Inside The Christmas Parcel?

What's inside? I don't know, do you? Is it . . .

A silver snowflake drifting towards the ground
Puffy Santa climbing down the chimney
A red, ruby nose that's Rudolph.

You think what's inside. What is it? Who's it from?
I don't know.
What could it be? Pressure building, soon you'll burst.
What is it? Getting near Christmas!
You're getting really excited.

I feel it, I rattle it,
I turn it upside down.
How I wish that Christmas morning would hurry up and come!
Presents, presents, presents!

Georgiana Macdonald (8)
Great Missenden CE Combined School

My Riddle

I am as silent as a tree in a winter glaze.
I wear a blue overall.
I am as transparent as the air.
People step on me and I ripple with their big Wellington boots.
I am alone in the world.
What am I?

A puddle.

Natasha Furmidge (9)
Great Missenden CE Combined School

Clubs

On Monday after school it was French
I was excited
My teacher said when I got there
'You're late.'
On Tuesday after school it was cross-country
I was ready
My teacher said when I got there
'Hurry and keep up.'
On Wednesday after school it was drama
I was okay
My teacher said when I got there
'Get in your group.'
On Thursday after school it was gym
My teacher said when I got there
'Press ups now, 1, 2, 1, 2.'
On Friday after school it was tennis
I was tired
My teacher said when I got there
'Do a rally with Jamie.'
It was Saturday.
I woke up.
I was thankful.

Charlotte Young (8)
Great Missenden CE Combined School

Winter Poem

There is snow sparkling like silver glitter,
Robins singing very sweetly,
It's like a sheet of sparkles,
It's like a cushion but freezing.
There's shining, sparkling, transparent icicles,
The house is covered in snow
Because of one winter's night.

Sophie Leese (8)
Great Missenden CE Combined School

The Flying Unicorn

F lying around with five horns,
L ying sometimes, flying other times,
Y oung unicorns normally die,
I gnoring the hunters,
N ight-time they fly, daytime they hunt,
G inger fringe and silver skin,

U nder trees in the wood at night,
N ight and day come once every 24 hours,
I n the night they hunt,
C rying for some food,
O r killing the enemy,
R unning for the prey,
N ight-time has come at long last.

Alistair Hull (9)
Great Missenden CE Combined School

Jungles

J ungles are
U nsafe, you should be
N ervous with
G orillas lurking in the
L ush leaves
E xercise is needed
S eriously.

Holly Broughton (8)
Great Missenden CE Combined School

Worm

W riggling
O n the ground
R ound and round he goes
M y wormy.

Danny McCree (8)
Great Missenden CE Combined School

I Asked The Little Boy Who Could Not See

I asked the little boy who could not see,
'What is colour like?'
'Why brown is like a tree stump
And green is like the summer leaves on a tree,
Orange is like the traffic lights
And yellow is like the sun,
Purple is like a thunderstorm
And violet is like a flower,
I think black is like night-time
And red is like a rose.'

Jessica Sweeting (8)
Great Missenden CE Combined School

What Am I?

I'm as small as a mouse,
I'm transparent but with flashes of colour like a ghost,
I'm as light as a feather,
I'm as round as a ball,
I'm as delicate as a china figure,
If you set hands on me, I'll pop like a balloon.
What am I?

Answer: A bubble.

Amy Walsh (9)
Great Missenden CE Combined School

Golden Leaves

On an autumn day
Yellow and green,
Spotted leaves
Falling to the ground.

Fraser Scarlett (8)
Great Missenden CE Combined School

What Is It?

It is as a wrestler
Whoosh like the wind
Breaking on the land like buildings falling down
It looks like the sky
It seems like a crab scuttling back to his hole
It sounds like a lion when angry
It feels like wet dew on a dry finger.
What is it?

Answer: the sea.

Flora Stevenson (9)
Great Missenden CE Combined School

Who Am I?

As soft as a pillow
As silver as jewellery
As sparkly as a star
As cold as an ice cube.
Who am I?

Answer: snow.

Harriet Samuels (8)
Great Missenden CE Combined School

What Am I?

I am as soft as silky snow,
I eat food as green as the grass,
I hop around like people,
I hate my dirty home,
I like it when it's clean,
My owner is as kind as me.
What am I?

Answer: rabbit.

Charlotte Wall (8)
Great Missenden CE Combined School

Christmas Is . . .

Christmas is people making snowmen
out of the glistening snow,
as others have a snowball fight
and sledging the frosty hills.

The decorations are up
on the emerald-green Christmas tree,
presents are under,
it's Christmas Eve.

Christmas dinner having turkey,
chewing on the tasty chicken,
with gravy and stuffing inside it,
yum, yum.

Opening the presents
under the Christmas tree
and having tasty sweets,
lovely orange and lemon juicy sweets!
Now it's Christmas!

Eloise Sear (8)
Great Missenden CE Combined School

What Is Colour?

I asked the boy who cannot see,
' What is colour like?'
And this is what he told me:
'Black is the shadow of a nightmare,
Gold is like a rich man's money,
Green is like smooth grass on a July morning,
Blue is a frozen puddle,
Red is a loving mother's heart,
Silver is a rich man's dream,
White is as beautiful as an angel,
That is what colour is.'

Meili Ellison (8)
Great Missenden CE Combined School

Smile Poem

Hair as hairy as a lion's mane
Face like a football
Ears as big as balloons
Neck as long as a giraffe
Breath as smelly as an ogre's
Nose as thin as a snake's body
Teeth as black as crow's feathers
Legs as tiny as an ant
Eyes as blue as the sky
Feet as huge as a giant's
Attitude as cheeky as a clown
Shoulders as tough as an American footballer
Body as thin as a tree.

Adriano Varriale (8)
Great Missenden CE Combined School

Christmas Parcel

What's inside the Christmas parcel? Is it -
a smooth turkey roasting,
a warm fire steaming,
a cute family feasting,
an ancient star flashing,
a glistening angel singing,
amazing cards shining?
I only wish I knew.

Cameron Hurley (8)
Great Missenden CE Combined School

School Poem

My story began on Monday:
The wood was black and gloomy,
The wind was whistling . . .
The teacher wrote a little note,
'You were never listening!'

My story began on Tuesday:
The sea was dark and cold,
Lightning struck on the beach . . .
The teacher wrote a little note,
'Your description is very weak.'

My story began on Wednesday:
The gladiators used to fight,
For the public's entertainment . . .
The teacher wrote a little note,
'Your neatness was a disappointment!'

My story began on Thursday:
In America a spaceship took off,
If I stood right next to it, it would give me a fright . . .
The teacher wrote a little note,
'There is no neatness in sight!'

Matthew Yeabsley (8)
Great Missenden CE Combined School

Summer

The sun beams over the mountains,
Like a gold coin shimmering in the air
In a warm breeze sweeping across the world.
The grass is olive green and the children springing everywhere
And all around you there is . . . happiness!

Maddy North (8)
Great Missenden CE Combined School

What's Inside My Christmas Present?

Yesterday I got a present
From my gran
I don't know if I can wait
I don't think I can.

I wonder what it can be
A talking snowman laughing
A red-nosed reindeer flying maybe
Santa Claus coming into my room
I'll just have to wait and see.

It's nearly Christmas morning
I'm tucked up in my bed
I can't get to sleep
Cos visions of Rudolph are flying through my head.

Thomas Burns (8)
Great Missenden CE Combined School

Bolt

For a horse he is high and fast,
Flashes through the field as fast as a cheetah.
Stops, creeps over to me, snorts
And I jump with surprise.
We charge together across the field,
At the end of the day we all go home
And sleep.

Caitlin Batty (9)
Great Missenden CE Combined School

The Writer Of This Poem

(Based on ' The Writer of this Poem' by Roger McGough)

The writer of this poem
Is taller than a mountain
As strong as a heavy rock
As gentle as a bird
As fast as a racing car
As slow as a turtle
As happy as a party
As silly as a clown
As clever as a king
As beautiful as a princess
As brave as a lion
As warm as a fire.

Annabel Beard (8)
Great Missenden CE Combined School

Miss Rose

Miss Rose is as kind as a fairy godmother,
She has lips as red as a rose,
Cheeks as pink as candyfloss,
Her hair is honey-coloured with chocolate highlights,
And is as curly as noodles,
Her eyes twinkle like stars at night.

Leena Alyedreessy (8)
Great Missenden CE Combined School

Colourful Leaves Haiku

In the morning sun,
Leaves red and yellow flying,
While I eat my bun.

Zoë Candale (8)
Great Missenden CE Combined School

Father Christmas

He is very, very jolly
   and always takes a sack,
To everyone around him
   and he is very fat!

His shining blue eyes
   are shining right now,
Everyone can't hear
   because he moves without a sound.

He's very, very funny
   and always eats pies,
Gets on his massive sleigh
   and then he starts to fly.

His scarlet-red suit
   has a belt around his waist,
Then he realises
   that he's got no time to waste!

Nick Wilson (8)
Great Missenden CE Combined School

The Writer Of This Poem

(Based on 'The Writer of this Poem' by Roger McGough)

The writer of this poem
is as fast as a lion
as slow as a tortoise
as happy as a kangaroo jumping
as silly as a puppy playing with his toys.

Sarah Hull (9)
Great Missenden CE Combined School

The Writer Of This Poem
(Based on 'The Writer of this Poem' by Roger McGough)

The writer of this poem
is clever as can be
as strong as a grizzly bear
as gentle as an ant.

As fast as a crook
as slow as a tortoise
as happy as a birthday boy
as silly as a clown.

George Cooke (8)
Great Missenden CE Combined School

I Am

I am as happy as a bird flying over the treetops,
I am as thirsty as a runner running his fastest,
I am as angry as a lion who didn't catch his prey,
I am as sick as a panda eating bamboo.

Hannah Cornish (8)
Great Missenden CE Combined School

Winter

On a winter's day
You can see the snowballs play
In the white blanket of fun.

Kirsty Line (8)
Great Missenden CE Combined School

Christmas Acrostic

C hristmas crackers cracking
H appy holly house
R udolph the red-nosed reindeer
I cy ice cubes in fridges
S tars twinkling
T insel on the tree
M erry mince pies
A ngel advent calendars
S anta's elves helping.

Joshua Carty (8)
Great Missenden CE Combined School

Lunchtime Argument

It's always in a lunchtime
when people have arguments.

It's always David and I
we go . . .
nip, nap, wick, whack, chatter, chatter, chatter
and we don't make up until the end of the day.

Jessica Gohl (9)
Great Missenden CE Combined School

Busy Street

Down a busy street
There are people shouting out
The cars go *beep, beep.*

Betsy Seal (9)
Great Missenden CE Combined School

My Best Friend

My best friend
Loves to sleep
Very peacefully.

My best friend
If shes woken
She'll howl and cry
Mournfully.

My best friend, like
Fudge with splodges of scrumptious
Rich, dark chocolate.

With ragged fur
She loves to play
Fun-filled.

She eats elegantly
Trots neatly
Bounds and leaps
Goes back to sleep and purrs.

My best friend
She's a cat
And her name is Carly.

Suzie McCarthy (9)
Great Missenden CE Combined School

The Thaw

The sun rose above the winter landscape,
The mushy snow nice and pure, crunching every footstep
And people steaming and shimmering.
Snowdrops, dropping minute by minute, starting to fade away,
Loads of icicles transparent, some disappearing,
Ponds and lakes have turned to ice
And water is dripping on houses.

Andrea Loftus (9)
Great Missenden CE Combined School

Untitled

This person is as loud as an orchestra,
As smelly as the dump,
Less funny than a teacher,
As cruel as a bully,
A smile as scary as a witch,
A nose like Pinocchio,
As slow as a snail,
Breath more revolting than an ogre,
As bold as a toad,
He is the worst person you would ever know!

Harley Richardson (9)
Great Missenden CE Combined School

I Saw Santa

I saw Santa - he was great flying in the air.
I saw Santa - he might have given me presents.
I saw Santa and he had a white fluffy beard with a jolly *ho,ho.*

Charlotte Debono (8)
Great Missenden CE Combined School

Snow

The snow is crunchy and creaky.
The snow comes down gracefully and gently to the floor.
The snow whistles past as snow fighting begins.
Children are playing, parents are shovelling.
Cars don't start, buses don't move.
Schools are shut.

Jack Elkington (10)
Grendon Underwood School

Glorious Snow

The glistening snow,
Fell through clouds,
Of pure white.

As it lay there,
Like a sleeping puppy,
Dreaming of its playmate.

Snow decorates the bare trees,
Snowmen laugh with happy smiles,
It lays icing on houses,
And imprisons you in your house.

With snow still drifting down,
Children make snow angels,
Have snowball fights in streets.

Dogs are barking, no longer is it quiet,
But all is well.

Helen Hewison (11)
Grendon Underwood School

Snow

The branches are covered in twinkling snowflakes,
Gently floating down, covering the Earth
With a white blanket of snow.
Children are laughing, making snowballs, having fun.
The snow brings joy to all the children.
Snow, the colour of a polar bear.
Hoping the sun will never come out,
As to live another day.

Yannek Benson (10)
Grendon Underwood School

Snow Poem

Hazardous, as the snow blizzards, blocking all roads.
The blanket invades, covering every inch.
Twisting, twirling, floating and swirling.
As the fairies dance, gently reaching the ground.
Suddenly, but magically, they blend and disappear.
Kids having fun, the schools are closed.
Only a robin is whistling.
It stands on the branch of a bare willow tree.
Its smaller branches in the gentle but frostbiting breeze, sway.
Traffic jams occur, accidents happen, some fatal.
Police urge people to stay off the roads.
Slowly but surely the centimetres grow higher.
Reports on the news of the big thaw
That is said to cause mass flooding.

Garreth Bayliss (10)
Grendon Underwood School

Funny Thing Snow

Snowball fights in the streets of Somerset,
People getting wet, long after the sun does set.
Cars become covered, sparkling icicles hang and gleam,
In the streets of Somerset.
Houses full of happy souls,
Having fireside to keep warm,
In the streets of Somerset.
Snow six inches high, fluttering past the window,
Forming a land of white,
In the streets of Somerset.
Snowball fights, children shout,
Somerset!

Jacob Wilson (11)
Grendon Underwood School

Snowfall

The sky turns white,
As day turns into night,
As crispy crystals fall.

Gritters come out from sheds,
When kids are in beds,
To salt the roads.

Snowflakes falling,
Ploughers hauling,
All the snow along.

In the morning,
While adults are snoring,
The angels and snowmen dance.

A blanket of glistening snow,
Reflecting, making a rainbow,
As kids play outside.

But the next day,
All the fun has melted away,
As children go back to school.

Shaun Hunter (10)
Grendon Underwood School

Fire

A small flame on a candle,
It got bigger and bigger,
The fire started to dance.

Fire sounds like wind,
Blowing in the breezes,
Hissing like a snake.

Fire looks blood-red,
The fire turned to ashes,
Leaving nothing left.

Charlie Hobbs (9)
Grendon Underwood School

Snow Day

Crystals falling to the ground,
Covering trees and cars,
Windows are frosted,
It creaks like floorboards under your feet,
Tastes like sour water,
Roads stop for first customer,
Gritman becomes a welcome visitor,
Corner shops become stained,
As the white crystals control the train tracks
And stop most transport.
Postmen struggle to get through the thick snow,
But children don't mind,
They just play,
They just build snowmen
And throw snowballs,
And a day off school
They don't mind.

Tom Baker (10)
Grendon Underwood School

The Shoe Collector

(Inspired by 'The Sound Collector' by Roger McGough)

A person came to my house this morning
and took every shoe in our city.
He took Mr Froud's brown shoes
and all the cool shoes from down the hall.
He took Mr Paul's shoes.
He went down in the mall,
he picked up four, but wanted more.
He went up a mountain
and drank out of a fountain.
He took every shoe in the city,
life will never be the same!

Rowan Wilson (9)
Grendon Underwood School

The Fresh White Layer

Dancing snow twirls through the icy air,
Falling, falling, settling onto its new world,
Soon-to-be melted away, again.
Still more flakes falling,
Making layers and layers,
Like a white sea with small ripples.
White trees, like skeletons wave around,
Snow creaking under thick boots,
Creak, creak, making thick footprints, big and small,
Children rejoicing, playing in the wondrous, white layer,
Angry people whose plane has been cancelled,
Motorists getting caught up in a furious blizzard,
But soon it will melt,
Melt, melt, melt away,
Soon to come back.

Emily Beebe (10)
Grendon Underwood School

Seashore

The sparkling ocean gleams in the sun,
A rainbow of fish race through the coral,
Deep down dolphins play,
The gentle sea reaches the shore,
And wets the soft, golden sand.
The splash of children playing in the sea,
The trickle of ice cream down someone's arm,
The drops of water from the river
Fall down a small waterfall
Into the wide, sparkling sea.

Fiona Wilkins (10)
Grendon Underwood School

The Frightening Fire

In a tiny part of Aylesbury,
People wandered throughout the town.
But nearby in a cottage,
There was fire spreading around.

As the fire came out the window,
All the family began to shout.
The mother flame was fading,
As her children spread about.

People started shouting, yelling,
As the fire spread about.
The children spread around and
Their dads tried to put it out.

Their mothers all gave up hope now,
They thought the fire had extended.
But their dads knew they were doing well,
Because the fire had ended.

The people stare at the remains,
Their ashes all over the place.
The children watch their toys burn,
With tears on their sad faces.

Charlie Carter (9)
Grendon Underwood School

Fire

Fire, fire, out the shire, through the wood
Growing higher.

Fire, fire, burning beds, shining ash always
Spreads.

Fire, fire, getting fire, burnt the wood and
The shire.

Fire, fire, is no more, people burning, people
Roar.

Richard Crossley (10)
Grendon Underwood School

Fire, Fire

Fire, fire, burning bright,
Fire, fire, gave me such a fright,
Fire, fire, in the night.

Fire, fire, burnt my home,
Fire, fire, it burnt my gnome,
Fire, fire, made me groan.

Fire, fire, burnt my bum,
Fire, fire, burnt my hot-cross bun,
Fire, fire, the killer gun.

Fire, fire, made me cry,
Fire, fire, made me fall and lie,
Fire, fire, made me die.

Joshua Boughton (10)
Grendon Underwood School

Snow

Snow, snow, everywhere,
Snow, snow, makes you stare.
All fluffy and white,
I dream about it every night.
Snow, snow, everywhere,
Snow, snow, makes you stare.
All snug in bed at night when,
Snow, snow, what a delight!
Snow, snow, everywhere,
Snow, snow, makes you stare.
Oh, how much I love it so,
One why does it have to go?

Jason Easton (11)
Grendon Underwood School

Snow

I have woken up,
I peer out my bedroom window,
And all I can see is white,
The ground is covered,
The trees are bare,
There's such coldness in the air,
I wrap up warm, gloves and scarf,
Go outside and have a laugh,
Snowmen, snowballs all around,
Time for angels on the ground,
It's time for bed,
So rest your head,
I wonder if the snow will be around tomorrow?

Emma Taylor (11)
Grendon Underwood School

Snow

The crispy, white snowflakes,
Landing on the bare trees,
To make them glitter in the sunshine.
Men leave footprints as a traipse
Through the crispy, white snow.
Children make big snowmen,
Leaving a path where the ball has been.
Cars slipping and sliding all over the white road.
Animals hibernating from the cold.
Then at the end of the day,
Time to go to sleep.
Will the snow be here tomorrow?

Emma Hirst (10)
Grendon Underwood School

The Massive Fire

Fire, fire, burning bright,
Fire, fire, full of light.
Fire, fire, killing people,
Fire, fire, will kill all.

Fire, fire, half a mile,
Fire, fire, had a style.
Fire, fire, did not stop,
Fire, fire, did not drop.

Fire, fire, I will die,
Fire, fire, flying high.
Fire, fire, killed my pet, Brad,
Fire, fire, hurt my dad.

Jake Kenworthy (9)
Grendon Underwood School

Snow

Snow slowly slithers around the busy world
Snow fiercely attacks the unprepared roads
Snow becomes angry
Snow immediately retreats and leaves children to have fun
Snow sees happiness
Snow sees danger
Snow sees sunshine
Snow slowly melts away.

Jamie Lipop (11)
Grendon Underwood School

Snow

Silently snow fell gracefully onto the tarmac ground,
Almost immediately little footprints appeared in the snow,
As children ran out of warmth and into coldness.
After a minute or so, snowball fights started,
The white blanket was ruined, but the children didn't care,
They were too busy having fun.
After a couple of hours the children returned home,
Not all went home though,
But when they did, they were glad to be able to wiggle their toes.
Winter was here, but much to everyone's dismay, it would not stay.

Joseph Michael Cronshaw (11)
Grendon Underwood School

Snow

The snow is calling you,
it's an invitation to play on its cotton-like surfaces.
When you step outside,
your feet crunch onto the world of candyfloss.
A spotless duvet buries the trees,
birds scavenging, looking for food, trying to keep warm.

Joshua Fradley (10)
Grendon Underwood School

The Frozen Child

As I peer out of my classroom, trapped like a hound,
The trees are brown but bare, the snow gliding from above.
I can see the children lying on the ground,
Gently flapping their arms and legs.
The lesson finishes and I take my first step on the snow,
My foot sinks an inch and I feel coldness,
My lord it turns white as I camouflage myself in the snow.

Connor Poole (10)
Grendon Underwood School

Teeth

The teeth should be white, shiny and clean
Use plenty of toothpaste don't be mean.
Brush the gums round and round
And then the teeth up and down.
Brush out the beef, potatoes and peas
And broccoli and carrots I had for my tea.
Apple pie and custard, crackers and cheese,
I need more toothpaste, give it a squeeze.
I'm brushing away the nasty plaque,
So my little teeth don't go black.
No holes, no fillings, no noisy drill,
No injections from the dentist, they really kill.
So I scrub and scrub and give them a rub,
Brush off the slime and smelly grub.
Floss in between my shiny teeth,
Just to make sure there is no beef.
I look in the mirror, I like my smile,
Don't call the dentist, no need to dial.
Just remember, brush twice a day,
Or else your teeth will decay.

Rebecca Johnstone (10)
Grendon Underwood School

Snow

Snow, a white tiger, prowling,
Glistening in the sunlight,
Smothering the ground with its ivory moss.
Creaking like floorboards with every step taken,
Like a creased shirt, ready to be flattened,
It lies, a white blanket, waiting.
Flakes pelt down, down, down,
A sea of white foam,
Covering the land, north to south.
Schools close, causing children to play happily
In the white layer.

Amy Kimber (11)
Grendon Underwood School

Orang-Utan Smuggling

Hunters prowling,
Orang-utans yowling,
Bullets flying,
Mothers dying,
Babies taken.

People buying
Orang-utans crying,
Being taught,
Having fought,
Giving in.

On boats,
Minds float,
To Indonesia,
Trying to please ya,
Finally there.

Horrible cages,
Waiting ages,
People shouting,
Sellers doubting,
No luck.

On tips,
No grips,
Being found,
Off ground,
Finally safe.

Didn't die,
Didn't cry,
Almost home,
Didn't moan,
Free again.

Eleanor Martin (11)
Grendon Underwood School

Snow

Snow, like a creased shirt,
Waiting to be trampled on.
Snow, like silver tinsel,
Sparkling in the glistening sun.
Snow, slowly drifting down,
As children happily spread their smiles.
Snow, crunching under feet,
Shuffling onwards as it's kicked.
Snow, like a white tiger,
Prowling round the chimney tops.
Snow, as fluffy as clouds,
Resting on the craggy mountains.
Snow, pure ivory white,
Making things look like cotton wool.
Snow, thinking like crystals,
Waiting until they touch the ground.

Kelly Batchelor (11)
Grendon Underwood School

The One Day Of Snow

It was silently falling,
Then slowly thawing,
The one or two flakes that came down.

Then in front of my eyes,
The snow filled the skies,
Like a swarm of dancing fairies, prancing round.

Then the dancing fairies lay,
Close together they stay,
Turning everything into a glistening white.

The very next day,
It had melted away,
As there had been lots of rain overnight.

Nicolle Kniebe (11)
Grendon Underwood School

Snow

Wandering slowly as it smothers the cobbled ground,
Leaving no sign of footprints,
Like a creased white shirt,
Which has never been ironed.
Lying still,
Like time had stopped,
Awaking children's faces,
Amazed with the sight of a white world.

Bursting into the fresh chilled snow,
Their sledges trailing behind them,
Their feet creaking on the snow like floorboards,
Which had sprung to attention.
Its plain, watery taste,
Like an ice pop with no flavour.

Quickening hail followed, stuttering onto the rooftops,
Bouncing onto the ground,
Spitting its last drops out,
It started to rain and rain,
Until all the snow was gone.

Danielle Brough (11)
Grendon Underwood School

Snow

I see snow when I look out of my window.
I touch flakes when I go outside.
Children build snowmen outside.
Cars get stuck in the snow.
I look out of my bedroom window and I see snow.
Dreaming of when I want the snow to come again.

Charlotte Fisher (11)
Grendon Underwood School

Snow

A white blanket covered the grass
All crisp and pale
A cold wind blew along the road
Snowflakes tumbled from the grey sky.
Children played in the streets
Picking up the white, crumbly fragments
And patting them into a ball with their cold hands.
Ice skaters glided confidently
Upon the frozen lake.
People wearing Wellington boots
Made a crunch as they walked in the whiteness.
Trails of sledge blades
Lined the grass and paths
Stalls on the corner of the street
Selling warm drinks and soup.
Happy couples walking about
Without a care in the world
The beauty of the snow was wondrous
But it was gone the next day.

Chris McMahon (10)
Grendon Underwood School

Snowfall

S now is fun
N ow it's time to go
O h, no snow today
W ater running down the road
F lakes coming down
A n angel from the sky
L ying in the snow
L ife is different in the snow.

Michael Goodwin (10)
Grendon Underwood School

Snow

Snow . . .

Like a creased shirt the silent covering lay,
so that the plants could no longer breathe.
It danced wildly in all directions,
till eventually it settled on the ground
like a foaming, frozen sea.
Spiny, thin skeleton trees stood alone,
staring at their bare branches,
icicles hanging down like gnarled fingers,
towards the white blanket beneath.
Tiny faces watched in glee at the white, glowing snow.
Wrapped up warm, they carefully stepped across the snow,
as if walking on creaking floorboards.
The still silence interrupted by the excited voices
of playful children.
The glistening winter sunshine breathes gently,
sending shining, golden rays to melt the crisp shirt.
Gone as quickly as it came,
the white turns to green.

Gracie Miller (11)
Grendon Underwood School

Watch Out There's A Fire

Leaping out of the enormous window came the spitting fire.
The grey smoke reached into the pitch-black sky.
The vicious flames swiftly grew higher and higher.

It was like a light bulb, bursting, with fire pouring out of it.
It is a bit like a boiling, crackling sauna being charged.
It was a doorway to a horrible death.

It is like a hot, haunted ghost that is dancing late at night.
It sways and waves against the sky and makes you sweat lots and lots.
Everything it gets to, it grabs and destroys.

Marie Rawlings (10)
Grendon Underwood School

Snow

The wail of Mum's car engine woke me up with a start.
I gazed outside to see a white, creased shirt, spread out
upon the ground.
I ran outside to hear and feel,
The crisp snow creaking beneath my feet.
Flakes of weightless ice settled peacefully on my warm tongue.
Clumps of snow hung precariously from branches,
Like white candyfloss clinging to the roof of your mouth.
The snowflakes, blowing wildly about in the wind,
Swerved and danced inside my ear,
Dimming the sound of the children playing next door.
I could see the snow on the ground rising,
As if it was alive.
It suffocated all living things beneath.
I threw clumps high above my head,
And started to leap about with happiness,
For it was the first snow we had seen for years,
And more was on its way.

Barney Riley (11)
Grendon Underwood School

Snow

As the snow lay there, crystals gleamed,
Roofs on houses were layered in beautiful blankets of snow,
Animals were cold, but fluffing up to keep warm,
Cars were just rolling down the road with caution,
Gritters drove down the road,
Trying to beat the snow from settling in.

Ben Whitehead (11)
Grendon Underwood School

Snow

Snow laid on the ground,
Gently falling down.
Neatly lay on the roofs,
Slowly melting.

The frost had covered the bare ground,
And glistening in the sunlight,
It had decorated the world.

The taste of a crisp snowflake,
Landing on my tongue,
Cold, melting.

The falling of flakes,
Children can hear.
Screams of laughter can be heard,
And the crunch once a foot sets in the snow.

Fingers freezing, snow cold,
Powdery, neatly laid,
Numbing cold.

Ellie Clarke (11)
Grendon Underwood School

Fire

A little spark jumped out of a fire,
Then it crawled along a wire.

It set alight a bit of wood,
Then burnt down the neighbourhood.

Loads of people were screaming,
The great fire was gleaming.

Connor Edwards-Bytom (9)
Grendon Underwood School

Snow

Snow, snow, falling down,
Snow, snow, landing softly on the ground,
Snow, snow, flying through the air,
Snow, snow, on people's head and legs.

Snow, snow, on TV on the weather,
Snow, snow, softly turning into ice,
Snow, snow, disappearing into water,
Snow, snow, evaporating to the sky.

Snow, snow, coming back from the sky,
Snow, snow, landing back on the ground,
Snow, snow, disappearing once again,
Snow, snow, that's the end of snow!

Jamie Rainsbury (10)
Grendon Underwood School

The Fire Of Twyford

It was Christmas Eve and in the middle of town,
Somebody was having a fire.

A few minutes later it grew and grew,
And caused the houses to burn.

Then the fire spread down the road,
And through the streets it grew higher and higher.

And everybody in the whole town,
Showed great concern.

In the middle of the night the fire stopped,
And most people had to retire.

Mia Riley (9)
Grendon Underwood School

Tragedy In London

The dancing flames tramped through
burning London,
Planting sparks in every direction,
Vomiting ruby-red fumes, flash,
Burning houses to smoking ash.

Smashing whatever objects that
get in its way.
Sapphire-blue flames shoot out everywhere.
In the field crows look for bread,
While all their friends lay down dead.

Jordan Petropoulos (9)
Grendon Underwood School

Fire, Fire

Fire, fire, burning bright,
Fire, fire, gives me a fright.

Fire, fire, burning down my house,
Fire, fire, shrivelled up my house.

Fire, fire, getting fire,
Fire, fire, getting power.

Fire, fire, getting lower,
Fire, fire, that's the end of that fire.

Max Brooks (9)
Grendon Underwood School

The Bonfire

Fire, fire, burning bright,
Fire, fire, making light.

Fire, fire, burning ashes,
Fire, fire, flicking lashes.

Fire, fire, what a sight,
Fire, fire, gives a fright.

Fire, fire, in the night,
Fire, fire, having a fight.

Fire, fire, climbing tall,
Fire, fire, might kill us all.

Fire, fire, reaching the sky,
Fire, fire, burning my eye.

Fire, fire, has long fingers,
Fire, fire, always lingers.

Fire, fire, calming down.

Laura Bell (9)
Grendon Underwood School

Fire, Fire

Fire, fire, burning low,
Growing larger each second,
So to the street we should go,
Some people had no desire.

Creeping, creeping, high and low,
Burning round corners, seeking through streets,
Creeping, seeking, here we go,
We are coming for you too, soon.

Keri Conway (9)
Grendon Underwood School

The Burning Rainforest

In a brushy rainforest a glowing spark glides,
All the animals sense danger and everybody hides.
The tiny spark evolves into a boiling fire,
Then it makes some flaming sounds
And invents its own choir.

It starts to destroy the forest hood,
Everything burns, leaves and the wood.
All the birds fly away to somewhere new,
Why? Because the fire went *shoo, shoo.*

All the bushbabies were very sad,
The fire changed to be very mad.
The fire flames start to rise up and up,
The fire now is larger than the world's biggest cup.

The fire has destroyed everything,
Now the forest needs a magical ping.
All the animals have lost their neighbourhood,
The fire should give the animals a new home, it should.

Mitchell Taylor (9)
Grendon Underwood School

Save Me

I know Mrs Avery,
She has a lot
Of bravery.
She saved me
From a shark
And now she has a spark.

Olivia Piontek (10)
Grendon Underwood School

To The Past

I went to the 1950s
They have wonderful kittys
They blew up a truck
And got covered in muck
And I went out of the 1950s.

I went to the 1960s
They have massive cities
I sat on a bench
And it turned into a trench
And I went out of the 1960s.

I went to the 1970s
It was so like the Twenties
I had a dive
And a person was so kind
And I went out of the 1970s.

Stuart Watts (10)
Grendon Underwood School

Fire

Fire, fire, blazing bright,
Fire, fire, burning light.

Fire, fire, boiling white,
Fire, fire, horrid sight.

Fire, fire, people shout,
Fire, fire, racing out.

Fire, fire, children die,
Fire, fire, people cry.

Adam Schofield (9)
Grendon Underwood School

Sunny Day Tanka

The sun is blazing,
As we sit and feel the breeze,
Having an ice cream,
Children playing joyfully,
Until the day is over.

Hayley Calow (11)
Grendon Underwood School

Seasons

I am hot,
They all love me,
When winter goes,
I come out.
What am I?

Ellie Culham (11)
Grendon Underwood School

Morning Joy Haiku

The dew is heavy,
The morning birds are tuneful,
Just after day breaks.

Sophie Hawker (11)
Grendon Underwood School

The Dragon's Ice Cream

The dragon's ice cream was swirled into every flavour in the world,
Into a magnificent mouth-watering flavour.
The crunchy bits on top were red as fire,
Like it was glowing a fiery red.

The dragon's favourite flavours were chocolate swirl
With scrumptious sticky toffee on top, cappuccino flavour, kiwi flavour
And strawberry and vanilla swirl with strawberry crunchy bits.
It looked like all of the world's colours were mixed into the one ice
cream.

This ice cream had all the feelings and all memory of the world,
And when the dragon took a lick of the mouth-watering ice cream
He was a whole different dragon!
He was much more kind than he used to be
And he even stopped eating burgers with extra grease on!

Amber Wieland (8)
Grendon Underwood School

Tragedy In The Street

Fire, fire burning bright
In the forest of the night
You tear down the trees in early light
From a window such a sight.

Women grieve to see offspring die
Fathers surrender to the determined fire
Children squeal for help through the smoke
Smoke and haze through the blaze.

Heather Carlile (9)
Grendon Underwood School

Bungle My Cat

Bungle is bonkers,
He's such a laugh,
He loves playing with conkers,
He hates having a bath.

His mum is called Lucy,
They both are so cool,
She's often called woozy,
They'd hate going to school.

Bungle loves his food,
His favourite is chocolate,
He's always in a good mood,
He's got such a hot look!

Rhianna Yapp (9)
Grendon Underwood School

What Is It?

Fast runner,
Food hogger,
Loud whiner,
Day sleeper,
Slipper ripper,
Post pincher,
Trick learner.
What am I?

(Answer: a dog)

Jack Daly (10)
Grendon Underwood School

The Wolf

Snow-covered muzzle,
Snarling, dripping in blood,
Coarse, rough fur - the wolf.
Developed muscles,
Its strength painted all over,
Oh, so brave - the wolf.
Sharp ears pricking,
Keen eyes staring at the hills,
Nose sniffing - the wolf.
Years of mystery,
Just gazing wistfully,
Such knowledge - the wolf.
The seasons pass by,
Winter, spring, summer, autumn,
All as one - the wolf.
Dampened, grey and black,
Fur of the wild, the greatest,
None like it - the wolf.
Sometimes he's yelping,
Most times he's howling in pride,
Triumphant - the wolf.
Yet he has some grief,
His broken heart is still there,
Can't forget - the wolf.
She left long ago,
So soon he too will join her,
Never more - the wolf.
The landscape is bare,
Pale white snow is all that's left,
No pawprints - no wolf.

Melanie Beckerleg (11)
Grendon Underwood School

An Alphabet Alliteration

A   An angry ape attacked Adolf the amphibian.
B   Bruce burped badly like a barfing bear.
C   Chris the cheese string crammed chips into his cheek.
D   Doris the dumb dork dropped dirty dice on Darren.
E   Edgar the egg was eating endlessly.
F   Frankie the freckle is friends with Fred the fence.
G   Golum gazed at his gelled, greasy and gooey hair.
H   Harry the hoover baked hake at a high temperature.
I   Iggy the iguanodon was an idiotic idiot.
J   Jake the jam jar had no jaws and was jaded.
K   Krusty kicked and killed Koopa the kennel.
L   Larry the leech liked the lemon-flavoured lake.
M   Mel the monkey missed her maths lesson.
N   Neil the naan bread nicked the nutritious nuts.
O   Olaf the orc opened the oriental crackers.
P   Percy the pilchard teased Pam the pork chop.
Q   Queenie quenched her thirst whilst questioning Quaver.
R   Ronnie the rabbit ate the revolting relish.
S   Saruman squeaked in a silly voice.
T   Tom the tuna fish tried to trick Trish.
U   Ugga the unfortunate ulna ushered Ugo.
V   Vonka the vase hated Venus very much.
W   Wilma the wafer waved to William the wheel.
X   Xenia the xylophone gave extra money to Xavier.
Y   Ying the egg yolk yanked York's tooth.
Z   Zelda the zebra lived in Zimbabwe.

James Michael O'Rourke (9)
Grendon Underwood School

Animal Alphabet

A nimals are absolutely awesome
b eware of big brown bears
c ats can cling and cats can stare
d ogs dance dangerously.

E nergetic eating apes
f ancy fidgeting playing plates
g anging gruesome great gorillas
h ungry handsome hairy tortillas.

I gnorant annoying angry ants
j umping ants in your pants
k angaroo killers on the loose
l ions saying dangerous moose.

M onkeys clumsily clinging
n aughty nanny goats singing
o ctopi eating apes
p oncey pretty playing mates.

Q ueens can dance
r ats can sing and prance
s nakes hiss handsomely
t ortoises chewing randomly.

U nicorns poking people with their sticks
v ery naughty nannies using toothpicks
w arty waving eagles' wings
y ellow cheetahs having races
z ebras all over places.

Hannah Darvas (8)
Grendon Underwood School

The Old Scottish Dragon

The fearsome, wrinkled dragon,
With his smoky breath,
He sat down playing a bagpipe
And choked himself to death!

Owen Bevan (8)
Grendon Underwood School

Alien

Do you smell?
Are you hairy?
Are you fair?
Are you scary?
Are you square?
Are you annoying?
Are you naughty?
Are you fast?
Are you a boy?
Are you a girl?
Are you big?
Are you green?
Are you fat?
Are you thin?
Are you mad?
Are you crazy?
Or is it just me?

Connor Day (8)
Grendon Underwood School

Banger Racing

Crashing
Big bangs
Scraping
Flying metal
Rolling over
Wheels bouncing
Buckets of water
Explosion
Fire brigade.

Kyle Carpenter (8)
Grendon Underwood School

Animal World

Dogs are dancing
Cats are prancing
Elephants are eating
Cheetahs are meeting
Rabbits are jumping
Fish are bumping
Horses are creeping
Hamsters are sleeping
Snakes are crashing
Slugs are bashing
Dolphins are swimming
Kittens are ringing
Goats are clapping
Rats are slapping
Cows are pretty
Pigs are witty.

Emma Owen (8)
Grendon Underwood School

The Sneezing Dragon

He lives in a cave.
When he sneezes he burns himself.
When he burns himself
He thinks . . .
I'll never do that again!

Jamie White (9)
Grendon Underwood School

Monster Fred

Fred is a monster
A monster he is
To his mum and his dad and his big sister Kid
They live under a river but they do have a lid
It is pretty leaky and they can't cope with it
Fred wonders how they cope with Kid
Their electricity is a bit faulty because it's controlled by water
Anyone who swam in their river they slaughtered
And ate as their roast dinner
And boulders and rocks as their roasts
Their cave looks like this
A big dump!
Fred's room is a big pile of feathers
Kid's room is full of sweeties
Mum and Dad's room is neat.

David Stow (9)
Grendon Underwood School

My Pet Turtle

My pet turtle, we named him Myrtle.
He lives in my room in a basket under my bed
With his best friend, Ted.
He eats pizza at Easter.
His favourite food is Bolognaise,
That is his silly phase.
I love my pet turtle called Myrtle.
He is a mad turtle and sometimes really bad.
His life is really sad.

Sophie Dormer (9)
Grendon Underwood School

Snow

The snow danced down from the heavens,
Leaving a white blanket over the world.
Flaky, crispy, nipping my fingers,
Decorating the sleeping trees.
Snowmen skipping through the crunchy snow,
Glistening in the moonlight.

Drifting from the fluffy clouds,
A white blanket over the world.
Soft, wavy on my hand,
Covering the tiny plants.
Snow angels dance over the ground,
Glistening in the moonlight.

Bethan Topliss (10)
Grendon Underwood School

On A Roller Coaster

Roller coasters are so fast, they zoom like a blast,
Up the loop, down the loop, around the loop,
And then you go up again
And then down so low underground
And then you see light again,
And straightaway another loop,
Up the loop, down the loop, around the loop,
And then you reach the station again.

William Dukes (8)
Grendon Underwood School

School Times

I have a friend at the school,
She's called Alice
And she lives in a palace.

She's very funny,
Just like a bunny.
She went to bed and banged her head.

She was so fine,
I thought she was mine.
She was so bad, she turned mad.

Niamh Malewicz (8)
Grendon Underwood School

Somersaults

I jump on the bed like a frog
I do handstands but I turn all red
Then I start to do somersaults
But I give up and go to bed.

The next morning I start all over again
I jump on the bed like a frog
Then I take a big breath
And run around like a dog.

Rosie Lord (8)
Grendon Underwood School

Jumping

Jumping high, jumping low
Jumping everywhere I go
If I jump to the sky
I feel like I can fly
I can't stop jumping
I will be lumping
I really, really love jumping!

Annie Lord (8)
Grendon Underwood School

Animals

There are lots of animals on the farm,
But what is in the actual barn?
The cows do a big loud moo
And they sometimes sleep in twos.
Horses gallop all around
And they try not to make a sound.
What is in the field?
Some woolly sheep
Trying to fall fast asleep.
Chickens lay some lovely eggs,
Their babies have wobbly legs.
Dogs jump all about,
Children do a big loud shout.

Jessica Walters (8)
Grendon Underwood School

Roller Coaster

Roller coaster, roller coaster
Round and round
Roller coaster, roller coaster
Don't touch the ground
I don't care where I go
I don't care if you're fast or slow
I could go round and round
I could go upside down.

Jacob Brough (7)
Grendon Underwood School

Daisy And Sooty

I have two very strange rabbits,
They both have eccentric habits.
For instance in the month of May,
They fell asleep for a day.

They tried very hard to confiscate a cat,
The next day they tried to fly like a bat.
Daisy landed on her poor little shoulder,
She fell on a great, grey boulder!

But whatever happens, I will always love my rabbits.

Beth Gregory (9)
Grendon Underwood School

Roller Coaster

Roller coaster, roller coaster
Going round and round
You're doing your job
At the fairground
It's great fun
It can go faster
Than you can run
It's the best ride in the world
When I went on it
It twirled and twirled.

James Coomber (7)
Grendon Underwood School

Mini D

Mini D makes me laugh
Eating bones from the bath
Doing what he wants to do
Trying to go to the loo.

Trying to be the best
But he needs to do the rest
Always in a rush
Trying to catch the dog school bus.

Mini D makes me laugh
Watching me in the bath
Coming to sleep with me
How happy can I be?

Mini D is really funny
With a grumble in his tummy
He always finds something to eat
And doesn't really like meat.

When Hannah came round to sleep
He ate her hair like a bit of meat
His favourite colour is black
With glitter on the back.

Shannon Eustace (9)
Grendon Underwood School

Carrots

C arrots is a soft, cuddly rabbit,
A rabbit you can rely on!
R acing in a field of mud,
R unning like a hare!
O bserving his orange carrots,
T asting his good food!
S craping out a rabbit hole!

Katie Lord
Grendon Underwood School

The Pet Collector
(Inspired by 'The Sound Collector' by Roger McGough)

A stranger came this morning
Dressed in silver and gold
He had a bag that was very noisy
He took my tortoiseshell kitten
The Wilson's black cat too
The Payne's black cat
And my dog too
My brown bunny rabbit
My brown and white hamster
My white guinea pig too
My tiny goldfish
My giant turtle too
My black gerbil
My slimy green snake too
My white rat
My hairy big tarantula too
A stranger called this morning
Dressed in silver and gold
He had a very noisy bag
There will be no fun in this house again.

Adam Best (9)
Grendon Underwood School

My Pet

My pet is a dog
Whom I love very much.
She sleeps like a log
And is soft to the touch.

Mathew Payne (9)
Grendon Underwood School

Silent Deer

Waiting silently in the sunny meadow stands the deer on the
swaying grass,
Listening to the whispering of the stream flowing beside him.
Thinking of the outside world and all the wonders that pass,
Watching the playing animals in front of him as the meadow gets dim.

Waiting silently in the dusky meadow still stands the deer on the
swaying grass,
Listening to the whistle of the wind all around.
Thinking of all the baby deer playing joyfully in the past,
Watching the hunter shoot the birds, as the sun sets
in the orange sky all around.

Waiting silently the sun sets in the meadow where the deer
still stands on the swaying grass,
Listening to the birds high in the trees, singing.
Thinking of the day behind him that flew past,
Watching the pink milkshake and feather clouds turn into darkness
when the wolves start howling.

Waiting silently in the darkened meadow sits the deer
on the swaying grass,
Listening to the silence of the meadow that is cosy and asleep.
Thinking of the shadows that look alive,
Watching the clouds that pass by the moon,
making a reflection of silver in the stream.

Zoe Malewicz (10)
Grendon Underwood School

Fire

Fire burning, crackling, sizzling,
Fire spitting, flaming, giggling,
Fire red, yellow, orange,
Fire dragon's breath flaming,
Fire blue, ruby fireball,
Fire ruby breath.

Robert Lane (10)
Grendon Underwood School

What's A Poem?

Should every poem rhyme?
Each single, boring line?
Or should the rhythm win,
And every word fit in?
Must it tell a tale?
Or will this method fail?
And how long should it be?
One line, two or three?
Or maybe this is wrong,
And a poem is a mass of ideas
Woven together with strands of imagination,
Sparkling moments,
Incorporated into the beauty of the words,
Thoughts and feelings.

Alex Black (9)
Grendon Underwood School

Pirates

P icking bones over Davy Jones
I f anyone tried to attack their ship,
   they would get the cannon and make it quick.
R udder's steering and the crew's cheering,
A ncient treasure is such a pleasure.
T hey sail around with no sound,
E ating crumbs while shooting guns,
S inking boats while theirs still floats.

Isaac Elphick
Grendon Underwood School

Winter

Snow falling down and down, round and round,
The wind howling and screaming,
The trees groaning with each blow of the wind.
Little animals running round and round,
Trying to find a place to sleep
And there you are snug as a bug in a rug
In front of the fire.
The warm glow of the fire
Makes you feel safe and happy.
You stay there for hours on end,
Just gazing into the fire.
You see lots of images in the flames -
A fire-breathing dragon in a cave
And a cute lion cub.
As the night gets darker and darker
And the flames die down,
You slowly go to sleep.

Abigail Randall (9)
Grendon Underwood School

Flint

F lint was always there when you needed someone to talk to,
L icking and nuzzling you with his soft, silky muzzle.
I used to ride him and he was very gentle.
N ot a bad tempered horse, but very cheeky.
T he best pony in the whole wide world.

Sarah Ackroyd (9)
Grendon Underwood School

The Colour Collector

(Inspired by 'The Sound Collector' by Roger McGough)

A stranger called this morning
Dressed in grey and white
And he said,
'What a colourful sight!'

He took all the paintboxes
And the pencils too,
He took the coloured sofa
And he took the coloured loo.
He saw my messy room
And sadly he changed it to white
And he said, 'It's not a colourful sight.'

A stranger called this morning
He didn't leave his name
And said,
'Life will never be the same.'

Emily Cudlipp (10)
Grendon Underwood School

Driver

D rivers are manic, especially when they're in a panic
R usty cars are no use to drivers
I ce on the road may sound trouble cos your car may end up
in rubble
V 8 engines are good for bumpy roads
E nd of the road, what shall we do? It looks like we're going
to crash
R oads can be foggy and watch out for that doggy!

George Howson
Grendon Underwood School

The Collector

(Inspiredk by 'The Sound Collector' by Roger McGough)

A stranger called this afternoon
Dressed all in blue and red
Put everything into a bag
Including the garden shed!

My teddies from my bedroom
The spoons from all the drawers
The settee from our front room
The brown and wooden doors.

The table from our kitchen
The chairs and the big TV
My pencils from my pencil case
I thought he'd even take me!

The flowers from the garden
The leaves from all the trees
The pages from my diary
The buzz-buzz-buzzing bees.

A stranger called this afternoon
Dressed all in blue and red
Put everything into a bag
Now I can't even sleep in my bed.

William Dearn (9)
Grendon Underwood School

My Best Friend

My best friend is called Shannon!
She is eight and her favourite colour is purple.
Her favourite food is pizza.
She is very good at swimming too.

Harriet Whitfield (7)
Grendon Underwood School

Monster

My monster is green
My monster is a baby
My monster is strong
My monster is funny
My monster is great
My monster is quiet
My monster protects me
My monster has big teeth
My monster is the best
Is yours?

Jordan Garrad (8)
Grendon Underwood School

Six Nations Rugby

The biggest kick,
The passing and throwing,
The sprinting people,
The hitting heads and banging,
The leaping people like dogs,
Injuries and tackling,
The ballerina ball spinning,
People winning,
Two teams playing,
The best sport in the world,
It must be *rugby!*

Tim Blackburn (9)
Grendon Underwood School

The Animal Collector

(Inspired by 'The Sound Collector' by Roger McGough)

A strange man knocked last night,
Dressed in pink and white,
Collected all the animals,
And took them out of sight.

The snuffling of the hog,
The barking of my dog,
The tapping of the lice,
The squeaking of my mice.

The miaowing of my cat,
The scratching of the rat,
The squirrel in the tree,
Always used to look at me.

The horse's neigh,
Now it's gone every day,
The singing of my parrot,
The munching when my rabbit ate a carrot.

The mooing of the cow,
The hooting of my owl,
The crunching of the goat,
When it ate my coat.

My pony called Lightning,
Was very frightening,
But now she's not here,
I'm full of tears.

All the animals have gone, why?
Every time I think about it, it makes me cry.

Ashleigh Doig (10)
Grendon Underwood School

Winter!

White cannons being fired,
From the snowboard army,
Snowmen being shot down.

Fires keeping people warm,
Jack Frost coming to nick your fingers and toes,
So keep snug in your bed.

Children learning to ice skate,
Others playing ice hockey,
Adults teaching children.

Polar bears cracking ice for food,
Seals swimming under icy seas,
Seals eating too much and getting fat.

Icicles growing quickly,
Icy lakes and rivers,
Ice fishing is fun.

Summer slipping off its shirt and shorts,
Winter wrapping up in its warm clothes,
Spring next, hopefully it will be beautiful.

Matthew Hawker (10)
Grendon Underwood School

Granny

My gran is old,
She walks about like a three-legged dog.
My granny is all wrinkly,
She makes me feel all tinkly.
But my granny is special,
Even if she is always the same.

Jack Boyden (9)
Grendon Underwood School

The Colour Collector

(Inspired by 'The Sound Collector' by Roger McGough)

A stranger called this morning
Dressed all in blue and white,
Put all the colours in a bag
And took them out of sight:

The greenness of the grass
The blueness of the sky
The yellow of the sun
The purple of my dye
The greyness of my pussy cat
The orange of the wall
The whiteness of the ceiling
The silver of my ball
The brownness of the carpet
The beigeness of the stair
The redness of the car outside
The goldness of my bear

A stranger called this morning
We did not see his face,
All he did was take all colours
Out of all our space.

Rahul Patel (9)
Grendon Underwood School

My Dream

When I go to sleep, there's someone there
Just whispering, whispering behind my dream

I can feel their breath just tickling my ear
And hear the gurgle of their voice
And the cackle of their laugh

So when you go to sleep
Just look out for that eerie whisper.

Evangeline Martin (9)
Grendon Underwood School

The Fun Collector

(Inspired by 'The Sound Collector' by Roger McGough)

A stranger called this morning
Dressed all in black and brown,
Put every bit of fun in his black bag
And carried it away.

He took the Game Boy
The football and the tennis ball,
The PlayStation 2
The football table.

The computer and the laptop
The whole box of Lego and K'nex,
The collection of cars
The skateboard.

The army soldier and remote control tank
The Beyblades and spinning tops,
The little zombie figures
The battleships.

A stranger called this morning
Didn't leave his name,
Left us with only boring things
Life will never be the same.

David Payne (9)
Grendon Underwood School

The Knife Collector

(Inspired by 'The Sound Collector' by Roger McGough)

A stranger called this morning
All in red and black,
He didn't come with manners
And just put the knives into a bag.

A stranger called this morning
All in blue and red,
He didn't stab me in the back
But stabbed my chair instead.

Jack O'Donnell (9)
Grendon Underwood School

The Colour Collector

(Inspired by 'The Sound Collector' by Roger McGough)

A stranger called this morning,
dressed all in blue and red,
put every colour in a bag,
while we were still in bed.

The brown of the tree,
the black of the cat,
the white of the snow,
my multicoloured mat.

The pink of my teddy,
the green of my drawer,
the orange of my jumper,
that I only just wore.

A stranger called this morning,
he was kind of mad,
took every colour in the house
and left us really sad.

Eleanor Rosier (9)
Grendon Underwood School

Ahh, It's Hallowe'en

A special night when kids dress up,
They go out at night, it's trick or treating time.
It is as scary as a real vampire suckling your blood,
Ghosts appear 1, 2, 3 - oh no!
It's a zombie!
So scary, what shall we do?
Bats squeaking, cats screaming,
What a thunderous noise and a horrible, dismal sky.
I want to go home.
It's as frightening as . . . ahh!
I'm turning into a revolting bat.

Charlotte Farrow (10)
Grendon Underwood School

My Dog

There was a dog with spots,
His mum loved him lots,
He loved his bone,
Liked to moan,
Off again he trots.

He's quite good for his fame,
Went in the newspaper again,
We didn't know,
He had a foe,
That had a strange name.

The enemy's name was Honey,
She actually was quite funny,
She bit his tail,
He gave a wail
And fell on his tummy.

Then he goes to the vet's,
Of course then he gets
Into big trouble,
At the double
And scared all the pets.

When coming home in the car,
We went into a bar,
When he came in,
He tripped over a bin
And everybody said, 'Ahh.'

So, then we came home,
We'd bought him a comb,
Showed it to him,
His face was dim,
Cos it had some foam!

Alastair Bayne (10)
Grendon Underwood School

Turtle

I am a sluggish mover,
I am a steady pacer,
I am a plant eater,
I am a slow chewer,
I am a deep thinker,
I am a shy hider,
I am a long survivor,
I am a house mover.

Natalie Tillman (11)
Grendon Underwood School

My Unicorn

The gold, fuzzy mane,
The silver, sparkly horn,
The unicorn will come when I whistle,
As she runs I love the way
The sound of her feet go clip, clop, clip, clop
As she walks across the road.
I love the way her bright yellow eyes shine in the sun,
And I love the way her lovely bronze tail is hanging down.

Olivia Barrett (9)
Grendon Underwood School

The Hurricane

The hurricane rushed around the town like lightning,
Destroying everything in its path,
Gates were ripped off their hinges,
And slates from rooftops were flying wildly,
The trees whipped in the rushing wind,
And leaves flew with the climbing cans.

Peter King (11)
Grendon Underwood School

Elephant

Tree crusher,
Bug stomper,
Leaf sucker,
Banana eater,
Loud shouter,
Water spitter,
Mud bather,
Rough player,
Angry looker,
Quick grower,
Fear fighter,
Good communicator,
Non talker,
People carrier.

Hollie Miller (10)
Grendon Underwood School

I Love You

You're as beautiful as a flower,
Your face gives my heart power,
Whenever I'm with you,
I don't know what to do.

You're as beautiful as a butterfly,
That flies in my head,
Your wings are so colourful,
They blind me until I'm dead.

Ryan Day (10)
Grendon Underwood School

DJ (Kenning)

Head banger,
Body flinger,
Dance producer,
Manly flirter!

Music maker,
Movement creator,
Drowsy worker,
Pop lover!

Ryan James (11)
Grendon Underwood School

Gallant Fire

Gallant fire,
Creeps upwards into the night,
Creating colours,
That never wish to die out,
Like our human peace.

Rachael Hodges (10)
Grendon Underwood School

The Blown Away Lady

There once lived a lady in Wales,
Who always got caught in the gales,
Just one day,
She started to hover away,
And was never again caught in the gales in Wales.

Alex Hirst (10)
Grendon Underwood School

My Ferrets

My ferrets are white and furry,
They've got sharp teeth but they're not scary.
I have to feed them once a day,
And I keep them warm with lots of hay.
I like to hold them every day,
Otherwise they bite me
And it hurts in every way.
I catch rabbits with them
And then they eat them.
So that's my ferrets,
I've had my say,
OK.

Will Cook (11)
Grendon Underwood School

My Favourite Book

I like books of all shapes and all sizes,
Books about animals,
Or maybe disguises.

Poetry books are quite good fun,
Or maybe English literature's your thing,
If you want, a book on shotguns,
Or maybe a book to help you sing.

But do you know what I like?
I like none of these,
I *like*
Adventure stories!
But I like the rest as well!

Rachael Sparkes (9)
Grendon Underwood School

School

School is boring,
Can't bear it anymore,
Wishing that I was by the seashore,
Don't want to be kept a slave,
Want to escape out the door.

I just can't wait till home time,
To be free and have ice cream,
To go and play football with the rest of my team,
Afterwards I'll watch television,
But I have to survive this day in 4A.

Matthew Priestley (8)
Grendon Underwood School

My Horse

The beautiful horse galloping in the sun,
Eating an apple delicious and ripe,
Getting sleepy in the day,
You have a bed of straw and hay.

Next day neighing happily, all is right,
You clever horse, happy all day and all night,
What a great day once again,
No one can say that you are plain!

Hannah Harris (8)
Grendon Underwood School

The Dream

The calm, turquoise ocean stays still once again,
The beautiful, gleaming dolphin appears in the far distance.
The bubbles are rainbows in pink, blue and yellow,
The sand sparkles like lots of diamonds under the turquoise ocean.
The multicoloured fish swimming relaxingly in and out of the
                                                    coral reef.

Shannon Ryan (10)
Grendon Underwood School

The Match

Getting ready to score some trys,
Starting the match,
People being tackled,
Rucks

Running to score some really good trys,
Throwing out from the side line,
Balls soaring through the air,
Players catching the rough ball.

Passing out from the scrum,
Running to score a try,
Whistle blowing,
Celebration,
Victory to us.

We won the cup!

William Beckerleg (8)
Grendon Underwood School

Einstein

Einstein was a lion,
    who made iron,
Einstein was neat,
    he was complete,
Einstein was clever,
    so he was made out of leather,
Einstein was sonic,
    that he found an atomic bomb.

Theresa Hurley (10)
Grendon Underwood School

The Football Game

Keepers crying
Balls flying
Injured people
Fans shouting
Balls soaring through the air
Shooting, missing
One more shot
Yes! It's there
Goooal!
1-0 to United
Five more minutes left to play
Referee blows
The final whistle
The end for today
United fans jump up in relief
Yes!
We won this time
Hooray!
They cheered!
We won
Our first match away!

Harry Protheroe (9)
Grendon Underwood School

My Dog

Hot summer's day walks,
Running in the sun.
Playing in the garden,
Having fun with everyone.

Lying on his quilt,
Stroking his golden hair.
Playing tug of war,
At the funfair.

Natasha Mason (8)
Grendon Underwood School

My Friend

My friend is called Shannon
Shannon is very funny
My friend has a dog
Shannon acts like a bunny.

Shannon has lots of toys
Especially her teds
She likes to cuddle them at night
But only in her bed.

She really likes to play out
Mostly in the snow
She likes to make big snowballs
But she is very, very slow.

Her favourite colour is black
Her favourite animal is a dog
Then it is a rabbit
And her dog likes to eat a chocolate log.

Shannon is very brave
And not afraid of anything
Shannon can be very funny
Especially when the doorbell rings.

Olivia Pettengell (9)
Grendon Underwood School

My School Is Cool

My school is cool, it really does rule.
It's really, really cool because it's got a swimming pool.
I've got some funky friends, their music really blends.
We are always rolling round and then we hit the ground.
I said I'd give her fifty pounds for her to tell me how it sounds.
She said it's really, really cool, now I know my school rules.

Katie Thomas (10)
Grendon Underwood School

Snow

C old snow lying on the ground
O ld men walking on the snowy path
L ittle children playing in the snow
D ad throwing snowballs at the little children.

S now is beautiful and white
N ow it's here we can go and play
O ld people throwing snowballs
W onderful snow lying sparkling on the ground.
          We love snow!

Zoë Ellison (8)
Grendon Underwood School

The Sun

The sun is like a fiery star,
A sparkling ball of hot ash,
It's high up in outer space,
Bright as a shining torch light,
More than 1000 miles away from Earth,
The sun is bigger than you could ever think,
So hot, no man has ever touched it.

Amy Jay (8)
Grendon Underwood School

Horses

Horses are in their stables,
Keeping cosy and warm,
As the farmers come along,
Cutting their lovely yellow corn.
The horses are eating the strong, green grass,
As other busy farmers pass.

Ilana Brock (8)
Grendon Underwood School

Snowflakes

Snowflakes white
Falling on the ground
Falling on trees
Whizzing round and around

Snowflakes white
As can be
Soft and melty
Soft as me!

Georgina Hearne (9)
Grendon Underwood School

Football

F ootballs flying
O ne team winning
O bvious goals
T ackling players
B ashing balls
A t the goal
L eaving the ball
L egs running left.

Nathan Whitbread (8)
Grendon Underwood School

My Beyblade

When I launch my Beyblade
It spins all day and night
When I try to stop it
It always cuts my fingers
When I have to stop it
I have to blow a deafening whistle!

Luke Boasman (8)
Grendon Underwood School

Favourite Things

A stupid monkey, a silly cow
However can they be like that?
I don't know!
A gooey cave, whatever next
A stupid clown, what a silly text
A funny frog hopping into the water
A sweet bird singing sweet music
A mad dog running all over the place
A sticky mouse sticking to my hand
A slimy snail leaving green slime everywhere
How strange! Oh, well!

Paige Hemming (8)
Grendon Underwood School

The Stars

The stars shiny and sparkly
Some stars are shooting stars
Fast, quick, fantastic
So light and bright
And good to glow
Stars, glittery and beautiful.

Ashley Thompson (8)
Grendon Underwood School

Environment

This is what is around us
Lakes, trees, bushes, reeds, grass
Lots and lots and lots of leaves
Twigs are on the ground
The sun is going down
The moon is coming up
Sssh, the night is silent.

Kieran Kendrick (8)
Grendon Underwood School

Racing Minis

Racing Minis is so cool,
I've always wanted to go,
But only my brother has seen one race.
He normally goes every month,
And brings photos back for me.

I always get a present,
Some people can get badly hurt,
Cars can go flying everywhere.
I can't wait till next time,
It's so cool.

Lucie Barnett (8)
Grendon Underwood School

The Rugby Match

R ugby's a rough game
U nderaged players on the bench
G irlfriends screaming for support
B etting who will win
Y outhful players storming down the pitch.

Ben Saltzer (8)
Grendon Underwood School

Rugby World

Group matches
World Cup
Trys and scores
Wins and loses
Balls flying
Broken bones
Fights and punches.

Quarter-final
Fights for trys
Scrums pushing
Kicking tense.

Semi-final
Tears and nerves
Rucks heavy
Boots stamping
Mauls pushing.

Final
Sobbing and bawling
National Anthem
Choir
Crowd's on edge
TV's on
Extra time
Nerve-racking
Dropkick
We won.

Celebration
Fans screaming
Awaiting next year.

Mats Venning (9)
Grendon Underwood School

Danger, Danger

At the bottom of the ocean the perilous, forgotten ship,
And there it stayed with the underwater world.
Horror, horror, that is all that comes to my mind now.
The captain and the suicide, the captain and the suicide.
As the scuba-diver crept closer and closer and closer,
The sound of danger ringing through his ears.
As the giant, bloodthirsty shark crept forward,
Then . . . *snap, crunch* . . . !

Jack Deering (10)
Oak Green School

Basketball

B ouncing, banging, bang, bang, bang, bounce, bounce, bounce,
A jump to win a point,
S houting all around,
K icking side boards in excitement,
E veryone happy,
T ime is running out,
B all goes through the hoop,
A win for the home team,
L ucky team,
L ucky, lucky, lucky team!

Sophie Sprowell (10)
Oak Green School

Spring And Friendship

Everyone is happy
Winter has gone
Spring is returning
Daisies, buttercups, roses and lilies are awakening
Animals come out to play
Children come to school
Shouting and screaming to their friends
When the whistle blows
Teachers talk to one another about their time off
As we get in we make new friends
And talk about our holidays
We learn new things every day
But this day is special
We learn about friendship
As it gets to lunchtime
We play on the perfect green grass
Girls do handstands
While boys play football.

Sheridan Richards (10)
Oak Green School

Flying In The Sky

Snowy owl flying high
Looking for a rat.
Snowy owl is riding by
Its wings spread out so flat.
But it's lost its feathers
Nothing to eat so throw out some heathers.
But you don't want to lose your head
Hurry up and go to bed.
Red and white cars
I count the golden stars.
After I read my book
I see a star shining so I have a last look.

Dale Scarlett (9)
Oak Green School

Snow

Snow is as flexible as a cushion.
Nobody can say that they don't like it.
On a sledge down a hill.
When it melts, do not cry
For the snow will come back next winter.

Snow is as beautiful as a picture,
Snowballs flying everywhere,
Icicles as sharp as a knife,
Children ice skating across the ice.

Snowmen standing very still,
Children sledging down a hill,
Children throwing snowballs,
Snow all over the walls.

The sun comes out,
The children start to cry,
Tears rolling down their faces,
I wonder why?

Tania Illahi (10)
Oak Green School

Friends

Over in the playground
I am waiting for my friends to arrive.
Some are fat
Some are thin
Some are tall
Some are small.
I like my friends
They are nice
I like to play with them
All day long.

Laura Shoult (9)
Oak Green School

Rose Of Pain

The rose that eyes look upon
With petals red as blood,
Is dangerous with its thorns of pain.
Prick your finger and you will bleed
And turn a repulsive green.
An hour later your body will morph into a stalk
And your head will become a rose.
You will start to grow into the ground,
Then for evermore you will be the *rose of pain!*

Jemma Gates (11)
Oak Green School

Snow

Snow is white like a white board.
It is slippery as ice.
It is as soft as paper.
Cold as frost.
It is all watery.
Smaller than a mouse.
It's all crispy.
I can skid if it comes again.
I can have a snowball fight.
When the sun comes it melts.

Haroon Humzah (9)
Oak Green School

My Days

I enjoy music,
I enjoy art,
I think that I am so smart.
On Wednesday music,
On Wednesday art,
We are smart.
On Monday it's piano,
On Tuesday it's play,
On Thursday it's Thursday Club,
On Friday it's rest.
When it comes to weekends,
It's time to visit family and friends.

Ieva Pakalniskyte (8)
Oak Green School

Pets

Cats purr
Cats eat
Cats lick their feet

Dogs play
Dogs fight
Dogs bark all night

Rabbits jump
Rabbits hop
Rabbits never ever stop.

Nadia Hibat (9)
Oak Green School

Snow Poems

Snow is exciting,
Playing joyfully with children.
Footsteps get the snow crunchy and crispy.
Snow is crawling and twinkling about.
The blue sky like the shining sea.
Snowballs.
Children love snowballs.
They can't stop playing.
Snow around me,
Crunching like crisps when people step.
Snow.
Tiny flakes
Falling on top of me.
Snow is prickly.
Snow comes in winter.
Goodbye, it is spring.

Maria Qaiser (8)
Oak Green School

Friends

I like my friends because
They are good to me.
They are kind to me.
They are nice.
My friends smell nice.
They are like sisters to me.
I've got friends.

Rheanne Gordon (8)
Oak Green School

Snow

Snow twinkling all about
It falls like a roundabout.
It falls all night
It falls all day.
Snow is beautiful
Just like me.
Snow has fallen
Playing night with me.
The sky is blue like the sea.
Snowballs being thrown.
Snowballs in someone's face.
Snow all around me
Crunching above me.
Snow with patterns
Snow falling around me.
Snow just sparkles
Like me.

Chelsea Davies (8)
Oak Green School

My Pet

My pet is cute.
My pet is cuddly.
She has different coloured fur.
She has a name.
You might think it's funny,
But it's Buffy.
She has a black spot on her chin.
She likes to jump on the bin.

Jody Collins (8)
Oak Green School

Snow

Snow is fun
I am dumb
Some are big
Some are small
Some are shaped
Some aren't at all
Some are sparkly
So are you
Falling from the blue
Round you
Some are crunchy
Just like you.

Karina Price (8)
Oak Green School

The Best School

My name is Hannah
I am a pupil
At Oak Green School
We are a happy school.

I like the snow
I like making snow fairies
I like snowball fights
We are the best school in the world.

Hannah Baldwin (8)
Oak Green School

Seasons

I love spring.
With blossoms blooming, all the trees are turning pink.
All the bushes are bare, children pick flowers for their families.

I love summer.
When the sun is gleaming,
Mum's sunbathing round the back.
Lots of flowers are sprouting.
I love summer and that is a fact.

I love autumn.
When the leaves are floating,
Kids are jumping in a heap.
The wind is blowing, making trees bare.
Loads of leaves we have to leap.

I love winter.
When the snow is gliding,
All the ground covered.
Lots of children are looking out the window
As the snow is silent
Not making a sound.

Tayla Brown (8)
Oak Green School

Snowy Poem

It is snowing today.
Me and my friends
Are having fun in the snow.
When it is snowing
We play snowball fights.
When I am walking to school
The snow is gliding to earth.

Michael Butler (8)
Oak Green School

The Snow

The snow falls down on me.
I love the snow.
When I go home
I chase about in the snow.
The sky looks like snow.
When it is snowing
I get excited.
The snow looks like white board.
When it's snowing
The snow falls down on the roof.
The snow falls from the sky.
Everyone is excited.
My brother is happy
Because he's never seen snow.

Amber Nasreen (8)
Oak Green School

Animals

I like animals.
They are really fun.
I like to play with them,
Over in the sun.

Some animals are furry,
Some have scales,
Some live in water,
Like sharks and whales.

Some live in the jungle,
Some live on farms,
Some, like horses,
Live in barns.

Lucy Warwick (8)
Oak Green School

The Rat, Bat And Cat

There once was a cat,
Who had a funny hat.
The cat saw a bat,
The bat saw a rat
And they all ran after each other.
And then the cat got a hat,
Suddenly the cat had a nap.
The rat had to put a blanket on
And when he put it on he fell asleep
And started to have a dream about sheep.
The bat went to the rat
And said, 'I want a nap too!'

Fakhra Khalid (9)
Oak Green School

The Old Man

There was once an old man,
He lived in a flat,
He wore a big hat,
He lived on his own,
All alone.
He had no family,
He had a wife named Lily,
She left him cos he was silly.

Katie Rogers (10)
Oak Green School

Flowers

Flowers smell
Flowers everywhere
Come in different colours
Red, blue, yellow
All the colours of the rainbow
Petals drop and scatter all around
See in the fields
Red roses of spring.

Clarice Farris (10)
Oak Green School

Snow

Snow is so bright
Now so cold
Out of my way
So the snow can get me
White snow is waiting for you
So come and play.

Marty Jeffries (9)
Oak Green School

Ancient Egypt

All the ancient tombs and mummies in the desert,
Buried underground with loads of treasures all around,
When excavators find it, they get really excited
And take it to the museums to get looked at by others.

Katy Warwick (10)
Oak Green School

Jabbermockery

(Based on 'Jabberwocky' by Lewis Carroll)

'Twas Monday and the staffroom inhabitants,
Did mumble and grumble in the office,
All shivery were the kids in the playground,
They were to be assessed!

Beware the topic test, my friend,
The questions that bite, the answers uncaught,
From the past until the end the children's scores . . . were
Naught!

He took his cartridge pen in hand,
Long time the questions' end he sought,
So rested he by the whiteboard tree,
And drew a while in thought.

And as in Xbox thought he sat,
The Dixon that with eyes of flame,
Came roaring down the corridor,
With Dominic to blame.

He thought real fast as she went past,
The permanent pen went drawy drawy,
All over her favourite old grey suit,
As she went screaming for no more(y).

And hast thou drawn on the Dixon, Luke?
Come to my desk, oh greatest friend,
Oh Saturday! Summer holiday!
Now drawing on teachers is the trend!

'Twas Sunday, and the staffroom inhabitants,
Did snore and snore in their beds,
All joyful were the kids at home -
Never to be assessed!

George Turner (11)
Oakley CE Combined School

Santa Wocky

Santa Wocky is busy in his workshop,
All his elves and friends are helping,
Mrs Wocky is pandering herself to get ready
For her ride in the sleigh.

Santa Wocky has got his eye on Oakley School,
To see if the children are being good or bad.
Santa Wocky looked down on the 6th December
To see Oakley School, but it was a Saturday.
Hey, who's that? It looks like another Santa Wocky.
He's a fake, I don't like fake Santa Wockys.

On the 24th December Santa Wocky got in his sleigh
And set off to jump down all the chimneys.
They finished up in the morning in Australia.
He set off back home to wait for another year
And then he can go back!

Phillippa Needham (10)
Oakley CE Combined School

In The Summer

Or a dolphin swimming wild and free
In the cool, clear blue sea
It swims around all day
Usually near Looe Bay

Maybe even a dog I could be
Scratching at every flea
I'd race around the moors until I was exhausted
Then go home to my cosy bed

Even a peacock standing proud
Squawking as I walk around
My tail feathers wilting like a willow tree
Oh, how proud I would be.

Felicity North (10)
Oakley CE Combined School

The Haunted House On Trinity Lane

Mary-Ann don't go there please,
You will prefer zits, lice and even fleas.

Why?
Don't go in the haunted house on Trinity Lane,
Whoever goes in comes out in pain.

Peter, don't go in that place,
Run away and pack your case.

Why?
Don't go in the haunted house on Trinity Lane,
Whoever goes in comes out in pain.

Sally, don't go near that house,
Go home to your little mouse.

Why?
Don't go in the haunted house on Trinity Lane,
Whoever goes in comes out in pain.

Shall I go in? It all depends
On, do I want to save my friends?

I went in the haunted house on Trinity Lane,
I went in and came out in pain.

Samantha Powell (11)
Oakley CE Combined School

Jabbermockery

(Based on 'Jabberwocky' by Lewis Carroll)

'Twas Friday and the giggling girls
Did gyre and gimble in the pool,
All mimsy was Mrs Jones,
Ben stuck up his hair and thought
He was cool.

Beware the swimming coach, my friend,
Her orders that snarl, her dives catch.
Beware the coach driver and shun,
The furious Mrs Dixon's snatch.

Bob took the vorpal slinky in hand
And chucked it in the air,
So rested it in the football tree.
Good job James had a spare!

And in home time in thought he stood,
Mrs Dixon with eyes of flame,
Came *marching*
Down the corridor.

One, two! One, two! And through their legs
The ball hit Luke Young, whack!
Reece scored and with the ball he came
'Gallumphing' back.

'Twas Friday and the giggling girls,
Did gyre and gimble in the hall.
All mimsy was Mrs Jones,
Ben stuck up his hair and thought he was cool.

Luke Young (10)
Oakley CE Combined School

Jabbermockery

(Based on 'Jabberwocky' by Lewis Carroll)

'Twas Monday and the naughty boys,
Did gyre and gimble in the hall,
All mimsy was Miss Noise,
And Mrs Science was studying a ball.

Beware of the music man, my friend,
He gets into some terrible moods,
His music will drive you round the bend,
Then he rushes home to eat his food.

The children in classroom four,
Had a teacher called Mrs Bone,
They sat down on the floor
And she had a deafening moan.

The children ran straight outside,
To play with all their friends,
Then one of them went to hide
And then they go to defend.

'Twas Monday and the naughty boys,
Did gyre and gimble in the hall,
And mimsy was Miss Noise
And Mrs Science was studying a ball.

Jade Varney (11)
Oakley CE Combined School

The Wind

I am like a howling wolf or a growling dog, but only when I'm angry.
When I am calm, I'm like a whistling bird or a purring cat.
I laugh uncontrollably at blowing old grannies' hats off and
turning umbrellas inside out.
I creep down the street looking for my next victim.
I blow away the clouds to welcome spring.
I can blow over lorries and strip trees bare of their leaves,
but then I stop to rest.

James Kilpin (9)
Oakley CE Combined School

Jabbermockery

(Based on 'Jabberwocky' by Lewis Carroll)

'Twas Friday and all of the girls
Were being very nice.
All of the boys were in detention
And the kitchen smelt of spice.

'Your maths homework is very late,'
One of the teachers did cry.
'But my dog ate it, Miss,'
One of the boys did lie.

The boys were playing football,
While the girls sat round in the cold.
Then all of a sudden it started to rain,
'All in,' shouted Mrs Sold.

The children walked in wet and cold,
The teachers sat drinking tea.
'It's not fair,' said a child so bold,
'They never think of me.'

The heating slowly dried them out,
As they sat in their crumbling classroom.
Their thoughts began to wander about,
Listening to Miss Noise.

'Twas Friday and all of the girls
Were being very nice.
All of the boys were in detention
And the kitchen smelt of spice.

Alex Jones (11)
Oakley CE Combined School

Christmas Wacky

Based on 'Jabberwocky' by Lewis Carroll)

'Twas Christmas at Oakley School,
And Santa Wocky had to come.
The children gith and gimbaled at the
Bazaar,
And the sleepy shepherd had just begun.

Our jabberwocky tree shines in the hall,
With the most beautiful ball balls.
On Saturday it was the Christmas bazaar,
The tree even lost its star.

The bazaar was busy, everyone was excited,
Santa Wocky had arrived,
He went to his grotto to see the children,
They were joyful as ever.

In the end they found the star,
And popped it upon the tree.
Everyone was happy, even the tree lit up,
And everyone cheered *hooray!*

Lara Trickett (11)
Oakley CE Combined School

Wind!

I am like a growling dog,
I am like a snorting hog,
I howl all day till the month of May,
I blow all the leaves off the very tall trees.

I swiftly glide through the town,
When I settle down
I am like a laughing clown,
I am like a squeaking mouse,
Scuttling through the house.

Bobby Grayburn (11)
Oakley CE Combined School

A Postcard From Barton Hall

To my friends

Weather's OK, but abseiling's fun,
Especially when it's in the sun,
Low ropes are fine when you co-operate,
It's really easy and really great,
The high ropes were too high to believe,
Phew! We had a harness, what a relief,
Chips, chips, chips all day,
I don't feel sick I'm glad to say,
The zip wire was the best,
I wanted to do it again and again, I didn't need a rest,
In the dark we had a swim,
The gentle water went over the rim,
The disco was fab, I sang all night,
I went dizzy in the multicoloured light.

My time here has been really cool,
Bye bye, Barton Hall.

Stephanie Bott (10)
Oakley CE Combined School

Water!

I like water
The crashing, whirly
The smooth and fresh kind
The hold-on-tight
Its deepest depths kind.

Force it out of buckets
Splash it all around
I do like water!

Laila Mankoo (11)
Oakley CE Combined School

Jabbermockery

(Based on 'Jabberwocky' by Lewis Carroll)

'Twas Friday and the silly boys,
Did gyre and gimble on the coach,
All mimsy was Miss Ellaby,
And Mr Music was singing with a crackling throat.

Beware of Mrs White,
As her voice might burst your ears,
Her teeth are sharp and will take a big bite,
And she's the worst of all your fears.

She took out her whiteboard pen,
'Your maths is late,' she cried,
She wrote upon the gleaming board,
The boy who had told a lie.

And as she marked all the books,
The boy looked at her in fright,
She shouted out loud,
'Come here young man and I'll show you a horrible sight.'

'Twas Friday and the silly boys,
Did gyre and gimble on the coach,
All mimsy was Miss Ellaby,
And Mr Music was singing with a crackling throat!

Bethany Francis (10)
Oakley CE Combined School

Jabbermockery

(Based on 'Jabberwocky' by Lewis Carroll)

'Twas Monday and the staffroom inhabitants,
Did mumble and grumble in the office.
All shivery were the children in the playground,
They were to be assessed.
Beware the topic test, my friends,
The questions that bite the answers uncaught,
From the past right up to the end,
The children's scores were naught.
He took his ballpoint pen in hand,
Long time the questions' end he sought,
So rested he by the whiteboard tree
And drew a while in thought.
And as in playing thought he sat,
The Dixon came with eyes of flame,
Came roaring down the corridor,
With Dominic to blame.
He thought real fast as he went past,
The permanent pen went draw, scratch, squiggle,
All over her brand new skirt
And she went screaming, no more!
And has thou drawn on the Dixon,
Come to my desk, my friend,
Oh! Frabjous day draw, scratch, squiggle,
Now drawing on teachers is the trend.
'Twas Sunday and the staffroom inhabitants,
Did snore and snooze in their beds,
All joyful were the children at home,
They were never to be assessed.

Luke Morris (9)
Oakley CE Combined School

Jabbermockery

(Based on 'Jabberwocky' by Lewis Carroll)

'Twas Monday and the annoying boys
Did grumble and gimble in the hall.
All mimsy was Mr Groys
And the girls were throwing a ball.

Beware the Fraction man my mate,
His quarters and halves that match.
Beware the Deputy owl and gun,
The evil haunting match.

She took her red gel pen in hand,
Long time the problem's end she sought.
So she rested by the sinks
And stood a while and thought.

And as in toughish she stood,
The Fraction man with eyes of greed,
Came doubling through the hallway doors
And strode with his dog on a lead.

She wanted to equalize with him,
To bring him down was her aim.
She'd catch him in the gym,
She'd make a plan but not get the blame.

She ran real fast as he went past,
And lured him in the gym.
She locked the door and at last,
She snatched the book of answers off him.

'Twas Monday and the annoying boys,
Did grumble and gimble in the hall.
All mimsy was Mr Groys,
And the girls were throwing a ball.

Laura Humphris (10)
Oakley CE Combined School

Jabbermockery

(Based on 'Jabberwocky' by Lewis Carroll)

'Twas Friday and the stressy teachers,
Were sat in the staffroom,
Drinking their cup of teeeea,
While Mr History sat in his toooomb.

Beware of the geography teacher,
Who will mutter for the world.
While Mr History stirred up a strew,
And the drama teacher did a twirl.

The children in Class 4,
Had a teacher called Miss Swoop.
They sat in class reading their book,
While Miss Swoop was eating her soup.

Mr Grumpy was in Class 2,
Teaching them art,
Although he was too grumpy to paint,
The children were very smart.

So everybody packed their stuffff,
On the hot summer's day.
We had all had enough,
So we went back home to play.

'Twas Friday and the stressy teachers,
Were sat in the staffroom,
Drinking their cup of teeeea,
While Mr History sat in his toooomb.

Gemma Clements (10)
Oakley CE Combined School

A Letter Poem

Dear Emma,
> How is your pink pig?
> Does it wear a wig?
> What does it eat?
> Does it eat meat?
> Did you say it now flies?
> Or are those just poor lies?
> Does it take food off the plate?
> Or does it climb the gate?
> I hear that it's talking,
> Or did you say it can sing?
> Love to see you soon,
> Perhaps some time in June.

Yours,
> Stevie.

Stevie Veil (10)
Oakley CE Combined School

Advertisement

Baby Bear tried to sell my porridge!
You don't want to buy my porridge because . . .
It's lumpy,
It's cold
And the stripes on the bowl make your eyes hurt.
It's a pain to cook,
It stains the saucepan,
If it's hot it burns your mouth
And nobody eats it.
But I do sometimes.
Go on, buy it if you want to, but remember . . .
Baby Bear tried to sell my porridge!
Signed:
> Goldilocks.

Katya Samson (9)
Oakley CE Combined School

Jabbermockery

(Based on 'Jabberwocky' by Lewis Carroll)

'Twas Thursday and all the girls were being told off
And the boys were playing chess,
Mrs Rice had a terrible cough,
Mrs Dixon ripped her dress.

Mrs Pardon made her cress,
Bobby gave Millie a jabbery kiss,
Class 1 made a wockery mess,
Mrs White let us dismiss.

A thunderstorm began to roar,
Then someone began to scream,
Mrs Durrant fell to the floor,
It was only Lucky having a dream!
The thunderstorm soon passed by,
The teachers drank their tea,
Class 1 stopped their cry,
One small child grazed her knee.

'Twas Thursday and all the girls were being told off
And the boys were playing chess,
Mrs Rice had a terrible cough,
Mrs Dixon ripped her dress.

James Lloyd (10)
Oakley CE Combined School

Santa Freaky

Based on 'Jabberwocky' by Lewis Carroll)

'Twas Christmas at Oakley School,
The pupils were performing in the hall,
The children mith and mamboed at the bazaar,
The tree even lost its star.

As Mrs Dixon began to speak,
In came the one and only Santa Freak,
Mrs Dixon fell to the ground
And the kids made a mithy sound!

As Santa Freaky saw the Christmas tree,
He fainted quickly in one, two, three,
Then the teachers got really mad,
They threw their handwags - how sad.

Dominic Russell (10)
Oakley CE Combined School

The Moon

Beams
As bright as a lamp in the dark

Sparkles
Like glitter on paper

Blaze
As bright as fire in the woods

Burns
Like the sun in the morning

Flare
So brightly it burns your eyes.

Sarah Olawale (9)
St Mary Magdalene Catholic School, Milton Keynes

Our World

Our world is round
It has sea and lands.
Our world is great
And we play brass bands.
Our world is huge
The grass and trees.
Our world has animals
And those stinging bumblebees.
Our world has great things
Like the great big sky.
Our world holds sun and rain
And in the sky birds fly.
Our world has so many towns
And so many different shops.
Our world is filled with great toys
And those tricky spinning tops.
Our world is great
I will always love it.
Our world holds everyone
And if I had to choose, I would choose
Our world!

Michael Yeates (9)
St Mary Magdalene Catholic School, Milton Keynes

Mr Pie Pants

Faster than a spaceship with a super fast rocket on the back
Hotter than a sun that has just been dipped in lava
Yummier than spaghetti and pizza with it
Scarier than a scream that always screams
Messier than the recycle area with cows poo on top
Taller than a million people stacked on top of a giraffe.

Aaron Derrig (8)
St Mary Magdalene Catholic School, Milton Keynes

What Is Orange?

Orange is the stars
Near Mars

Orange is the sun
Eating a bun

Orange is a fruit
With a boot

Orange reminds me of sand
Playing a band

Orange reminds me of a beach ball
Being hit in a hall

Orange is a fish
On a dish

Orange is a good colour
So get it on your book cover.

Evie Butler (8)
St Mary Magdalene Catholic School, Milton Keynes

Hamsters

H appy
A mazing
M unching food
S tores food
T iny
E ating food
R uns round in a wheel
S mall.

Hayleigh Maxey (9)
St Mary Magdalene Catholic School, Milton Keynes

Scary Scattered Surroundings

Why am I scared?
The world around me is taunting.
It haunts me and somehow will always trace my footsteps,
A detective,
The popular disguise for my antagonist.

The world is a dragon,
Constantly spitting fire,
Bullets are whirling around in the harsh hurricane of war.

Peace is my idol,
Peace is a harmless orphan searching for perfection,
It is a gift that God has given us,
Though no one is prepared to unwrap it,
The wrapping paper,
A splash of mud from a revolting field,
Wrapped in the Devil's disguise,
Peace stands so silently effected by the stillness,
Never ever forget but remember not to judge a book by its cover.

Eventually God's gift will be unwrapped,
Peace will be revealed,
Then it will defeat my scary scattered surroundings.

Tatiana DeSouza (10)
St Mary Magdalene Catholic School, Milton Keynes

What Is Orange?

Orange is my cat that runs around in a circle
Orange is a grapefruit that makes my tummy gurgle
Orange is paint that goes slush
Orange is a carrot that wants to blush.

Maxwell McCarthy (9)
St Mary Magdalene Catholic School, Milton Keynes

The Moon

The moon always shines as bright as the sun,
It also shines like a giant white bun.

It gleams like a sparkling jewel,
Surprisingly to you it might look like a silver ball.

The moon glows an everlasting torch light
And when it's not a full moon it looks like a giant has taken a bite.

The moon also shimmers like a clear river flowing
And could make a spell on the wind for blowing.

The moon sparkles like a lot of glitter,
The stars are its belt and will sometimes flitter.

Michael Tacticos (8)
St Mary Magdalene Catholic School, Milton Keynes

What Is Pink?

Pink's jelly that wobbles in my belly.
Pink is a peach that is sitting in a bowl.
Pink is a fairy's wing that flutters in the wind.
Pink is a feelings that makes me happy inside.
Pink is a lily on the lake.
Pink is a fizzy drink at a party.
Pink is a case you can put your pens in.

Molly Hodgson (10)
St Mary Magdalene Catholic School, Milton Keynes

The Moon

Shines
Like the sun that shines all day

Gleams
Like a bright, bright star in the dark, dark sky

Glows
Like a shining ring on a lady's finger

Shimmers
Like the sun that people sunbathe in

Sparkles
Like the good glitter in people's hair.

Victoria Bates (8)
St Mary Magdalene Catholic School, Milton Keynes

All About Football

F ast
O ffside
O wn goal
T oe punt
B ench
A ngry
L oud
L ong.

Glenn Amofa
St Mary Magdalene Catholic School, Milton Keynes

What Is Green?

Green is the grass
Where I like to ride my bike
Green is the grass
Or an apple that I like.

Carl Hennessy (9)
St Mary Magdalene Catholic School, Milton Keynes

The Moon

Shines like a very shimmery star,
Like the very bright sun,
Glows like a gigantic firefly
In the darkness,
Blazes in the night
Like flashing car lights and sparkling fire,
Gleams like an enormous diamond
In the darkness,
Sparkles with light in space
At night.

Emilio Baqueiro-Blucher (8)
St Mary Magdalene Catholic School, Milton Keynes

The Moon

Moon, moon you shine like a light,
Shines like a star,
Sparkles like a star,
Glows like the sun,
You sparkle like glitter.

Annmarie Tong (8)
St Mary Magdalene Catholic School, Milton Keynes

The Moon

The moon is as bright as gold,
The moon shines more than diamonds,
The moon gleams more than swords,
The moon gleams like lightning,
The moon sparkles like water.

Salvatore Mulé (8)
St Mary Magdalene Catholic School, Milton Keynes

The Moon

Shines like a bright light
on a winter's night

Gleams like snow freshly fallen
on the ground

Glows like pearls
freshly made

Shimmers like water
with the sun shining on it

Sparkles like teeth
that have just been cleaned.

Alicia Cascone (8)
St Mary Magdalene Catholic School, Milton Keynes

Summer

Summer is when the summer queen awakes from her winter's sleep,
She calls to the sun to awaken,
To bring light to this winter's end,
She calls to the flowers to spring out into colours for all to see,
She blows her cool breezy breath to wake us all to the fresh air,
She smells of fresh dewdrops as she passes to welcome the
Butterflies, rabbits and other creatures,
But she only ever comes in summer
Because winter is when she sleeps,
This is not the end of summer,
Summer comes and goes.

Olivia Bates (10)
St Mary Magdalene Catholic School, Milton Keynes

Down And Lower

Anger!
A bucket of madness, dripping with shame.
A vein bursting pain, incensed.
Someone driving you up the wall.
A temper will make you rage.
The furious, horrid thing taking you over.
You are a livid creature that was annoyed.
An irate rain of fury.
You are enraged with the world.
A flame of furious fire.
Flaring around you.
Angry but sad.
Angry!

Ricardo Martuccio (10)
St Mary Magdalene Catholic School, Milton Keynes

The World Of Shame

My feet sink through the sand
No one to pull me up
There is no entrance nor an exit
My life is a shell waiting to be crushed
Angry with anger, shameful with shame
No one to talk to, no one to look at
I feel like a mat and no one cares
This is my world of shame and anger!

Nathan Quail (11)
St Mary Magdalene Catholic School, Milton Keynes

Loneliness

Loneliness is a gloomy white puddle
I slip and slide
A street of shivering shaky fears
Anger and shame to me
My loneliness is a shadow
She swipes past in the misty night
In all the darkness of shame
The lamp post is a person shining and thinking shame
She found no escape
Full of emptiness
No one near
No one beside me
Cold street of fear
In the street alleyway
Darkness is at my side
Loneliness!

Koral Sayles (10)
St Mary Magdalene Catholic School, Milton Keynes

Valentine's Day

Once upon the fourteenth of Feb,
Many people are to be wed,
As chocolate and flowers are to be sold,
Cupid's arrows were flying so bold,
This could only mean one thing,
That Valentine's Day is here again.

Luke Hodgson (12)
St Mary Magdalene Catholic School, Milton Keynes

Friends

Friends make you feel special,
Cheer you up when you're down,
Always make you laugh and smile
And will always be around.

When you have problems on your side,
They will always help you through
And when you're feeling lonely and glum
They will always be with you.

Friends make you feel warm inside,
They are helpful and special too,
I don't know how I would live without one,
It must be unhelpful and sad.
Humm?

Vanessa Alifoe (10)
St Mary Magdalene Catholic School, Milton Keynes

The Classroom

The classroom is a realm of torment
Tempting and teasing
When you are alone you become disorientated
When you're not it is magical
The whining windows scare you silly
The screaming SATs shake your mind
The classroom with its bleeding blackboard
The tape recorder plays with your mind
The classroom is a realm of torment.

Nicholas Machin (10)
St Mary Magdalene Catholic School, Milton Keynes

Seasons

Summer
When I wake up in the morning and see the sun shine,
A warm summer feeling goes down my spine,
I know when it's summer when the garden is in bloom,
When the barbecue is out and so are we too!
Long lazy days just soaking up the sun,
Sitting by the pool and having fun.

Autumn
Autumn has come and starting to chill,
Leaves are falling upon the hill,
Red and brown leaves beginning to fall,
Leaving the trees bare and tall,
Wildlife are hurrying to store their grub,
The bushes have got their berries on to do just that.

Winter
Winter is here, cold and dark,
Ice on the lakes, ice on the river, the ducks can't swim, they just skate,
Children excited, snow on the way,
They're dreaming of sleighing and snowman building again,
'Christmas is here and Santa is on his way, hooray.'

Spring
Birds are singing and flapping through the air,
Shoots are popping up everywhere,
Dew in the morning, showering the spider web,
Washing and dusting here and there,
Lambs are playing in the fields,
Buds are forming on branches of trees,
Cherry blossom out and make me sneeze.

Katie Shine (11)
St Mary Magdalene Catholic School, Milton Keynes

Alone

Nobody to go to, nobody needs you
The reflection in the sea of sadness doesn't want to care
Unwanted, uncared for, unneeded, unloved, unknown of
A piece of a puzzle lost and forgotten
A hand without its fingers
A face without its features
A mind without its thoughts
A gift of speech without the knowledge to use it
A life without its soul
Loneliness.

Bianca Scorer (11)
St Mary Magdalene Catholic School, Milton Keynes

Secret

Tell me your secret
I promise not to tell
I'll guard it safely at the bottom of my mind's well

Tell me your secret
Tell me, tell me please
I won't breathe a word
Not even to the bees

Tell me your secret
It will be a pebble in my mouth
Not even the sea will make me spit it out.

Ben Freeman (11)
St Mary Magdalene Catholic School, Milton Keynes

Babies

Their fat little bottoms all wrinkly and soft,
Their tubby wee bellies bulge over the top
Their toes are so stumpy, miniature size
I really love babies they open your eyes

They gurgle and splat at your every noise
Their arms waving madly, throwing their toys
Dummies go flying, bottles do too
When you're near a baby be careful will you

Babies don't care if they're fat or slim
In fact they don't care about anythin'
Who's going to feed me is all they want to know
I just want some grub to make me grow

With bellies all full and burps out the way
It's time for their sleep at the end of the day
Heavily breathing in their cots at night
A sweet sleeping baby is a wonderful sight.

Taylor Soden (10)
St Mary Magdalene Catholic School, Milton Keynes

The Moon

The moon gives out light
Like a light bulb
The moon blazes like a firework
The moon shines like a bright light
The moon shines like the sun
The moon glows like a crystal.

Christian Alifoe (9)
St Mary Magdalene Catholic School, Milton Keynes

Who, What, Why, When

Who, what, why when

Who are you?
I see your face in the crowd, glaring at me
I recognise your face, similar but only to me!
What are you doing here?
What did you come here for?
Should I be glad?
Why?
Do you want to see me?
When did you come here?
When are you leaving?

When I saw you glaring at me in the house of mirrors
Who are you?
What are you?
Why are you?
When are you?

Is it me? I see my reflection.

Chloe Gibson (10)
St Mary Magdalene Catholic School, Milton Keynes

Fairground

Dragons flying in the air,
Swish, splash, squirty squid,
A toy for boys and girls,
Just for kids - no kidding!
Laser liquid, doggy dodgems,
Haunted mansion - eyes pop, brain squash,
Teddy trembles if you touch,
Earthquake starts when giants march,
The fairground gates are opening up!

Natalie Chan (11)
St Mary Magdalene Catholic School, Milton Keynes

Happiness

Happiness is light lifting laughter,
Always by your side.
Helping you bloom out of your cocoon,
Shapes you for your way.
Happiness is the answer to your problems,
But it has its ups and downs.
Always trying, trying, trying,
To help you win your way.
Happiness is your friend,
Following and helping you.
Happiness is light lifting laughter,
Happiness is my friend.

Kieran Clarke (11)
St Mary Magdalene Catholic School, Milton Keynes

Yellow Is The Colour Of Summer

Yellow, yellow, yellow, such a happy feeling
Yellow makes everything prance in the sunlight
Yellow makes the world seem big and full of love and happiness

Winter makes the world seem small and lonely
Quiet secrets of long lost dreams
Winter makes summer seem small
Where everyone's comments do not count
One thing that I am looking forward to is summer!

Danielle Klar (10)
St Mary Magdalene Catholic School, Milton Keynes

The Shadow Cat

The shadow cat is a cheetah, dashes in the night
Trash can to trash can, searching left and right

But deep in the alleyways, you'll always hear that
Courageous cat on the move
Staring and hissing, always trying to prove
That he is number one and don't mess with him
Always bold and independent, showing that he is not dim

But careful, the shadow cat knows all and watches your every move
Scattering and scurrying finds things faster than you can find
A future seeker you might think he is
And a seeker of the mind.

Holly Matthew-John (10)
St Mary Magdalene Catholic School, Milton Keynes

Angry

A ball of burning fire struggling to get out
Spitting flames of fury
A volcano exploding, getting everyone in sight
Covers everyone with burning words
A boulder on a catapult, ready to fire
A flinging fist of fury
Covered with nails and spikes
Ears steaming like a pot of hot water
Angry, yes - but hurt as well
Angry.

Meelie Clarke (10)
St Mary Magdalene Catholic School, Milton Keynes

Lonely

No one is with me - there never is
Always behind, never in front
Confused - with anger, all packed up with shame
A black room full of fear
When time never moves on
With no sound or movement
But barbaric breathing
I'm all alone and always will be.

Michael Williams (11)
St Mary Magdalene Catholic School, Milton Keynes

The Moon

Beams
As bright as a lamp in the dark

Sparkles like glitter on paper

Blazes
As bright as the fire in the woods

Burns like the sun in the morning

Flares so brightly it burns your eyes.

Chloe Osei-Bonsu (8)
St Mary Magdalene Catholic School, Milton Keynes

There Is Something In The Cupboard

There is something in the cupboard
I don't know what it is
I'm really, really frightened
Let's get on with our showbiz
Let's find out
Because I'll get
Scared it might
Be a
Dinosaur, a spider
With long legs
Bugs or caterpillars
With really long teeth!
You never know what
It is if you don't
Open the door! It may be
A sticky thing covered with
Tomatoes, carrots and yucky
Stuff, big, slimy
Chewy, furry
Yummy, yukky
Skinny or
Maybe a
Big, disgusting
Lava man
Just open the door and you'll find out! Don't doubt yourself . . .
Crickety crackety . . . the door had opened, all slimy and yuck
It was a thing that I couldn't touch . . . it was a dinosaur!
But then I realised it was just my dad.

Edward Finn (8)
St Mary Magdalene Catholic School, Milton Keynes

My Friends

I have lots and lots of friends,
Our friendship never ends,
We are always together no matter what we do,
We sometimes get into fights,
But only just a few.

My friends mean a lot to me,
We don't always agree,
My friends are always there for me,
That is why my friends are my friends
And we will stay together till the end.

We play too, we laugh and cry together too,
But we are friends and that is what friends do,
We tell each other secrets
And that is all about my friends.

Orlaith O'Hanlon (10)
St Mary Magdalene Catholic School, Milton Keynes

Hobbies

Hobbies, hobbies, planes, trains
The mains of the all the planes
They never complain
It sounds insane
But you can imagine
It eating a cane!
Every train has its name
And watches a lot of David Blaine
The planes say David Blaine is really lame
The trains say take the pain
Then you can't do it like David Blaine.

James Barrett (10)
St Mary Magdalene Catholic School, Milton Keynes

Headmistress

Being sent to the headmistress
Is hell for some,
Yes, but I've been good,
The only one.
Walking along the corridor,
Looking at the staff,
Making funny faces always makes me laugh.
Spinning, turning, twisting too,
Like a buzzy bee jumping free.
You burst in the office,
Jumping with joy.

But if you've been quite bad,
That's another thing.
Walking and walking,
Making a good lie,
Just if plan A busts
And then you start to cry.
Sighing and yawning,
Listening to the same old lecture,
You look at the bad boys and girls wall
And there is your picture!
My favourite place!

Anna Atkins (10)
St Mary Magdalene Catholic School, Milton Keynes

I Love Dolphins

Dolphins live under sea
And they dance with glee
Dolphins are incredible and excellent indeed
They dance and prance all around
The water.

Esther Adewuyi (9)
St Mary Magdalene Catholic School, Milton Keynes

Anger

My anger grows
Like an ever-growing plant
I wanna break something
But I know I can't
My anger dies down
But rises again when I see his face
I wanna punch and kick him
And banish him from the human race
He's really irritating and cocky
He makes me wanna shout
I have to beat my mattress senseless
To let it all out
But I should of known
He'd start a fight
Why doesn't he leave me alone
And let me sleep at night?

Cameron Lockhart (11)
St Mary Magdalene Catholic School, Milton Keynes

What Is Blue?

Blue is the colour we see in the sky
Blue is the coldness
And the shiny bright eyes
Blue is the saddest person with tears hanging down
When I eat a blueberry it goes down my blue uniform
Blue is a shiny thing I like at night
And all I do I think I might need to look
Around the site.

Victoria Pickford (10)
St Mary Magdalene Catholic School, Milton Keynes

The Dragon

Its breath as hot as hot as half the sun
Its curvy swaying tail
Its eyes two round balls in their sockets
Its skin as hard as a knight's chain mail
. . . The dragon

Its claws are really sharp, as sharp
Its nose a breathy mass
Its teeth sharpened to the sharpest point
With the end of a knight's old sword
It would not be nice to pass . . .
. . . The dragon

Its scales are green with patches of red
Saliva drips from its fangs
It uses golden coins to make its bed
Its scales are slimier than a newt's tail
. . . The dragon.

Kate Hollins (8)
St Mary Magdalene Catholic School, Milton Keynes

Autumn

Autumn is golden red and orange,
It tastes like carroty mash and sweet sausages,
It sounds like falling leaves and swirling wind,
It looks like a colourful rainbow and a swamp of leaves,
It smells like a fresh bonfire and sweet leaves,
It makes me feel cuddly and snug.

Hannah Smillie (8)
St Mary Magdalene Catholic School, Milton Keynes

The Moon

Shines
Like thousands of bolts of lighting, making houses spark

Glows
Like a candle's flame burning better than a flame-thrower

Shimmers
Like a star in a bright sky

Sparkles
Like glitter on somebody's face

Gleams
Like a diamond in the sky.

Connor Lauderdale (8)
St Mary Magdalene Catholic School, Milton Keynes

The Mysterious Girl

At night she has gleaming eyes
In the day she has none
She is a cat prowling around at night
Sleeping in the day
She is nocturnal and shy
Not many people see her
Not even her mum and dad
She disappears when people come near
She is terrified, hungry and looking for somewhere to sleep.

Louise Crabbe
St Mary Magdalene Catholic School, Milton Keynes

The Moon

Radiates light
As bright as the sun in the sky

Is as conspicuous
As a crystal in a cave of darkness

As lustrous
As a leather chair

Flares like lights in a dark room

Glossy
Like a star in the universe at night.

Joshua Gentry (9)
St Mary Magdalene Catholic School, Milton Keynes

The Kids Dream

If kids were teachers there would be no detention
If kids were teachers there would be no hard work tests
If kids were teachers you could never get zero on a test
You would always get a 'well done'
If kids were teachers you would be in your own clothes
If kids were teachers there would be a TV in every classroom
With a Sky box and free reading time
If kids were teachers they would be better than the grown-ups!

Ross Johnstone (9)
St Mary Magdalene Catholic School, Milton Keynes

The Moon

The moon is as still as a kettle
It's like a snow angel
It's a bright light
Is like the sun shining on water
It's a magic ball
It's as heavy as a thousand trucks.

Elliot Moore (8)
St Mary Magdalene Catholic School, Milton Keynes

Willy Wonka

W illy Wonka
I nteresting to know about
L ovely little man
L earnt how to make chocolate
Y oung man

W ise man
O rganised everything
N oble person
K ing of chocolate
A mazing attitude.

Fraser Green (8)
St Mary Magdalene Catholic School, Milton Keynes

Bonfire Night

Fireworks are sparkly red and shimmering blue.
It feels like hot lava and boiling sparklers.
It smells like hot marshmallows and warm cake.
It tastes like candyfloss and hot chocolate.
It sounds like *popping* pans and popping *big* balloons.

Bethany Conway (7)
St Mary Magdalene Catholic School, Milton Keynes

The Poodle

There was an old man named Doodle,
He had a fluffy pink poodle.
He has a good mate
Who was always late,
But always brought him a noodle.

Olivia Hodgson (8)
St Mary Magdalene Catholic School, Milton Keynes

Charlotte's Web

C alm
H appy
A nxious
R esponsible
L ovely
O riginal
T ricky
T ender
E xciting
S ilent

W idow
E legant
B rave.

James Cochrane (7)
St Mary Magdalene Catholic School, Milton Keynes

Trapped

Trapped in a box
With nowhere to go
With a brain of gold
And a heart of steel
Cries of sadness and cries of hope
With immortalised darkness
And light disorientated by fear
What is wrong?
I'm lonely with my ego alone.

Ryan Gray (10)
St Mary Magdalene Catholic School, Milton Keynes

The Fairground

The fairground smells like sticky toffee apples,
It looks like a fun electric park
With all the fancy flickering lights,
It feels so exciting your heart flutters like mad,
It sounds like people screaming with excitement -
Very, very noisily,
It tastes like candy cane, candyfloss
And very sugary sweets.

Sarah Gatley (8)
St Mary Magdalene Catholic School, Milton Keynes

The Grumpy Old Woman

A grumpy old woman from MK
Drove to see her cousin, May
She slipped on a chain
She then got a pain
And she had to go home on the train.

Joanna Lloyd-Knibbs (7)
St Mary Magdalene Catholic School, Milton Keynes

Rain In Spain

There was a young woman in Spain
Who really was quite a big pain
She ran far, far away
They screamed hip hip hooray!
Then it poured from the heavens with rain.

Katy Worton (7)
St Mary Magdalene Catholic School, Milton Keynes

Lonely Stranger

Lonely,
No one beside or on the inside
Behind, in front, nothing there but selfishness
I've already met, my life, wasted, not new, it's old
I've already tasted the bitterness of my lonely life always
Growing, causing misery that is not forsaken all for me a
Lonely stranger, a wandering danger!

Cameron Green (10)
St Mary Magdalene Catholic School, Milton Keynes

Christmas

Christmas looks like lots of white fluff
And crystals falling from the sky.
It feels like cold ice cream and frozen glass
It smells like crispy flowers
It sounds like bells ringing
And people singing Christmas carols
It tastes like hot chocolate and marshmallows.

Lisa-Maria Lamprecht (8)
St Mary Magdalene Catholic School, Milton Keynes

Animals

A frican elephant
N ewt
I guana
M ammals
A ntelope
L ions
S nakes.

Lucy Freeman (9)
St Mary Magdalene Catholic School, Milton Keynes

An Alien World

Big stiff branches
That never move
A big pool of slimy
Sloppy goo
And a reflective
Upside-down sky
With fishy orange clouds
A sideways slippy
Ice road
My garden!

Kirby Haddon (8)
St Mary Magdalene Catholic School, Milton Keynes

Dolphins

Dancing dolphins across the sea
Prancing and glancing and looking at me
Dancing dolphins here and there
Dancing dolphins everywhere
If you don't believe me, take a look and see
See the dancing dolphins as happy as can be.

Sophie Luckett (9)
St Mary Magdalene Catholic School, Milton Keynes

The Silly Man From MK

There was a silly man from MK
He was going shopping today
He bought bubblegum
Then he slipped on his bum
Then he jumped up and shouted 'Hurrah!'

Aine Lavelle (7)
St Mary Magdalene Catholic School, Milton Keynes

Favourite Things

I like music because it is cool
I like Westlife, they never play the fool
Those are a few of my favourite things

I like basketball, football too
I like playing games, how about you?
Those are a few of my favourite things

I like sweets, chocolate, many things to eat
I like fizzy drinks but they are only a treat
Those are a few of my favourite things

I like animals like dogs and cats
I like kittens, puppies and sometimes rats
Those are a few of my favourite things

Those are all of my favourite things.

Emily Smith (10)
Seer Green CE Combined School

Favourite Things

I like rings and kings and all sorts of things,
Presents and greed for all of my needs,
Those are a few of my favourite things.

I like sweets and treats to have to eat,
A chocolate heaven and a drink of seven,
Those are a few of my favourite things.

I like wheat and honey and lots of money,
I'll click my fingers, get cash in a flash,
Those are a few of my favourite things,

Yes these are a few of my favourite things.

Daniel Brennan (11)
Seer Green CE Combined School

Holiday Hooray!

Hooray, hooray!
At last, a holiday.
At the beach from dawn to dusk
Or a private swimming pool just for us.

Hooray, hooray!
At last, a holiday,
A posh hotel from Heaven above,
Brand new sheets, white as a dove.

Hooray, hooray!
At last, a holiday,
France, Italy, Greece and Spain,
I've been there once and I will again.

Hooray, hooray!
At last a holiday,
Have some fun, share some joy,
Doesn't matter if you're a girl or boy.

Hooray, hooray,
At last a holiday,
Not France, Italy, Greece or Spain,
But camping in Wales and rain, rain, rain!

Roisin McNeil (10)
Seer Green CE Combined School

A Walk In The Park

I am Sam the silver dog
Waiting for a walk
The door opens to reveal a path
A bright gunmetal colour
The park lies ahead of me
I am a dog in the park

It's a bright sunny day
The sky is a blanket of blue
I look down to see
The fresh green grass
I wag my tail with all my might
I am a dog in the park

The trees are tilting to a side
And the sun has a smile on his face
The cloud pounces
And covers the sun
The light has gone away
I am a dog in the park.

Alex Damas (10)
Seer Green CE Combined School

Holiday

It's a holiday, it's a holiday
I'm flying in a plane
It's a holiday, it's a holiday
I'm zooming on a train
It's a holiday, it's a holiday
I'm sitting in a car

It's a holiday, it's a holiday
We are finally going far.

James Howkins (11)
Seer Green CE Combined School

The Seasons' Flowers

They are all so beautiful
In many ways.
All different colours,
Never the same.

Tulips, pansies, petunias too,
Forget-me-nots are always so blue.
Purple pansies, crimson roses, ochre buttercups
To smell with your nose.

To me nothing can beat
The wonderful smell that is
Just a treat and the colour
Of the lavender!

It is my favourite flower,
It dances in the summer breeze,
Without a care in its leaves!

For those are the flowers of the summer
All beautiful each
In their colour.

Catherine O'Brien (11)
Seer Green CE Combined School

Favourite Things

A rainbow in an amber sky
A dreamland packed with fun
A robin on the window sill singing its merry song
A couple holding hands and walking on a beach
A warm fire on a snow-filled Christmas night that seems so deep
A memory of a summer holiday with a friend or my family
A candlelit dinner on February 14th, just a girl and me
Now these are my favourite things.

Harry Evans (10)
Seer Green CE Combined School

Seasons

The harsh winter whips the trees,
Stripping them of all their leaves.

With help from autumn that turned them brown,
To make them easier to pull down.

Then the spring comes to mend,
With brand new leaves to help defend.

From the spring to summer breeze,
As it rustles through the trees.

Then the summer trees fruit they bear,
From the rosy apple to the lime-green pear.

So from the white of the winter to the brown autumn leaves,
To the pink of spring blossom to the blue summer breeze.

Jessica Gamble (10)
Seer Green CE Combined School

Spring

Spring, spring comes once a year,
Daffodils, snowdrops remind me of spring,
The little green buds that start to appear,
Spring, spring comes once a year.

Spring, spring comes once a year,
Lambs, chicks remind me of spring,
The puddles of water all become clear,
Spring, spring comes once a year.

Spring, spring comes once a year,
Brand new animals remind me of spring,
Small baby rabbits with their soft ears,
Spring, spring comes once a year.

Amy Quelch (11)
Seer Green CE Combined School

Seasons

Let's start with spring,
A season with the fun of lambs,
The burst of the daffodil,
A season where the sun comes out
And brings the butterflies.

Then comes summer,
The sun is always out,
Water shimmers in our pool,
It's a season where everyone is happy,
Everyone's outside having fun.

Along comes autumn,
The sun starts to go,
Leaves turn crimson and brown,
Flowers die, conkers fall,
But it's still a great season for us all.

Winter slowly comes along,
Brings the Christmas cheer,
Snowflakes slowly touch the ground,
This season brings a smile on everyone's face
As they see presents under the tree.

Seasons are special from sun to snow,
Seasons bring smiles
As they come and they go.

Sarah Popely (11)
Seer Green CE Combined School

Seasons

The autumn wind whistles among the trees,
Leaving nothing but empty branches,
Covering the ground in bronze leaves,
But it will always come again.

The winter snow drifts,
Wandering through the house tops,
Ice hangs longingly from the gutters,
But it will always come again.

The spring blossom turns pink,
Petals open in the sunlight,
Apples turn all red and juicy,
But it will always come again.

The summer heat covers the world,
White clouds cover the blue sky,
Apples start to drop off,
But it will always come again.

Jennifer Rothwell (11)
Seer Green CE Combined School

Catz

Sleep, eat, purr, bite,
That's all they do all day and night.

Bite, eat, sleep, purr
And occasionally they groom their fur.

Purr, bite, sleep, eat,
Not just their food but Mum's best meat.

Eat, purr, bite, sleep,
They find your hat and it's theirs to keep.

As you can see,
All cats do,
Is make someone happy
And that is you!

Charlotte Pearce (10)
Seer Green CE Combined School

Seasons

The winter is a cold season
A harsh season
A nothing grows season
December will shout
January will scream
And February will dream
Winter is the cold season

The three gallant knights
Come to the rescue
March, April and May
Are their names
Spring is the grass green season

Summer is a hot season
An ice cream season
Swimming in the sea season
Summer is the crimson season

Autumn is a crisp season
A crunchy, munchy season
The golden leaf season
You'll have a good time
In the golden season.

Daniella Camilleri (10)
Seer Green CE Combined School

Seasons

December, January, February
The snow fell out of the sky
Heads turned as it fell on by
The wind blew in the blocks of flats
And blew off the old man's hat
This is what I remember

September, October, November
The leaves, the leaves all around
Red, bronze, falling to the ground
This is what I remember

June, July, August
The sun made blistering heat
So we take ice cream to eat
People swimming in the sea
All my friends playing with me
This is what I remember

March, April, May
The rain is gone, the sun's here
The blossoms soon to be near
Animals soon to be born
Their mothers eating fresh corn
This is what I remember

January, June, March, September
August, July, May, November
April, February, October, December
These are the months of the year
So this is what I remember.

Laura Babb (11)
Seer Green CE Combined School

The Seasons

In winter the ground is cold
The sun shines weakly down
Making the snow glint gold
Snowballs are being thrown
From dawn to dusk

In spring flowers are blooming
Baby animals are being born
Birds are prancing and grooming
The weather starts becoming hot
From dawn to dusk

In summer the sun shines a lot
The grass turns yellow
And flowers are blue, red and violet
It is now hot
From dawn to dusk

In autumn leaves start falling
Amber, crimson and gold
Birds again are calling
It's getting colder
From dawn to dusk
The seasons never change.

Katrina Johnson (10)
Seer Green CE Combined School

The Seasons Of The Year

March and April, May
These months make up spring
The sun peeking through, the flowers in bloom
And new life for me and for you

June and July, August
These months make up summer
The sweltering heat and ice creams to eat
With the butterflies fluttering by

September, October, November
These months make up autumn
With the leaves falling, the temperature too
It marks the beginning of winter

December, January, February
These months make up winter
With all the snow and bitter cold
The freezing of the earth

The seasons go fluttering by
Year after year they go
Never changing, never ceasing, never leaving.

Stephen Rosser (11)
Seer Green CE Combined School

Rhymes Of The Seasons

Winter is like a nasty witch
Who prods us with her knife
The land gets masked with ice
We need gloves and scarves at this time

Spring is a fun time for play
The sun is like a candle
Yet the storms pelt us with rain at this time

Summer reminds me of the beach
Or a kind and loving king
Enjoyable, warm and hot days
And party time.

Autumn is a fun time
With colours in the leaves
Red, orange, amber, fun to jump into
And rake them up again, a beautiful time.

Philip Grudier (11)
Seer Green CE Combined School

Pets

I like pets
They hate the vets
I go to the park to play
They run away
I get cross
When they get lost
I take them home
They chew a bone
We go for a walk
And to people I talk
And say
'That's my dog over there
We play all day.'

Alex Hayes (10)
Seer Green CE Combined School

Seasons' Crusade

January's cold wind whips around the bare trees,
The fog lies thick, master over the battered land,
February brings green shoots struggling out,
The drowsy sun warms slightly wrestling against the thick
foreboding clouds,
March makes forest clearings flood with bluebells,
An army pushing out winter's weakened dictatorship,
April comes in proudly dressed in full,
A gown woven of spring's wonders, a headdress of daffodils
and tulips, spring's jewels,
May comes with angelic lambs and yellow fluffy chicks,
Pink blossoms adorn the trees, the green leaves peep out for their first
view of this changing world,
June brings fields with lush green grass and sunshine,
A tinkling stream gurgles by carpeted with gorgeous white lilies,
July brings smiling children and sweltering heat,
Foreign sun shines fiercely down as the summer holidays dance along,
August comes with summer's full glory challenging the
lurking rumours of winter's invading army looming nearer,
September makes summer's flowers fade,
The once vivid colours have paled to ill ivory,
October makes leaves swirl down, carpeting the woodland floors,
The last trace of summer disappears and dies,
November brings a fine vapour of eerie mist enveloping the trees,
Autumn fights its last battle before it falls and winter's
dictatorship rules,
December makes the angel-white snow with its shining brilliance,
Its cruel slippery iciness with the snow drifting so thick and powerful,
winter's demons at work,
Winter, spring, summer, autumn each make a stand
Fighting for their chance to control the land.

Emma Campbell (10)
Seer Green CE Combined School

The Four Seasons

Winter
When winter comes it is bitter
It is cold

Spring
But as soon as spring blossoms
All is filled with warmth

Summer
The blazing summer sun comes out
As soon as can be
And we might go off to some distant land

Autumn
The leaves, the leaves all around
Russet, bronze, gold and brown
Are all the autumn colours

Another year has passed by, gone
Passed by.

Edward Avery (10)
Seer Green CE Combined School

My Dog

My dog is a giant
He is very defiant
And as strange as a bear
With very red hair

He has eyes as big as the moon
Which stare all round the room
He has a tail as long as a bus
But doesn't make a fuss

His tongue is wetter than a river
When he licks you, you shall shiver
His paws are as big as a shed
We all get squashed when he gets in bed.

Jack Leeper (11)
Seer Green CE Combined School

Fairy's Favourite Things

Pretty purple dressed in lilac,
Long curly hair, no questions about,
Bare feet, none of my mum's high heels,
She has slim and petite wings,
That's one of my favourite things,
Is that yours too?

One day Prince Charming will come,
On a spotless white horse,
I live in a tower with gold gleaming hair,
He's definitely one of my favourite things,
But he's not yours, he's mine.

Reading, dancing, talking and singing,
I will take them up as a habit,
So my calendar is full,
I just live to fly,
So here on the hedge top,
This is my song.

Georgia Davis (10)
Seer Green CE Combined School

My Pony

Trot, canter, gallop, jump
Sit up straight into jumping position
Gallop, canter, trot, walk
Whoa boy, whoa
Slow boy, slow

Come on Copper we can make it
Extended trot over the plain
Uh oh there's a log
Over we go sand flying into his mane

Trot, canter, gallop, jump
Sit up straight into jumping position
Gallop, canter, trot, walk
Whoa boy, whoa
Slow boy, slow

Come on Copper let's go back home
Just a few minutes away
Slow down boy, oh what a fab ride
Today what a fab ride today.

Amy Zelepuken-Smith (10)
Seer Green CE Combined School

Seasons

In the spring the flowers are blooming
Yellow, pink and green
The bluebells are blooming in the dark woods
As the roses are glowing red

In the summer the colourful butterflies
Are fluttering round the park
The blazing red sun is hotter than ever
And the flowers are jade and amber

In the autumn the leaves are falling
The leaves are turning ochre and
You can see hats and gloves

In winter the ground is cold
The sun peeps down through the clouds
And all you can smell is nice hot mince pies.

Joe Clarke (11)
Seer Green CE Combined School

Big Or Small

Cats are tall
Insects are small
Whales are big
Stick insects look like a twig
Giraffes are large
Bulls charge
Giants are really tall
Ants are really small
But we
We're all different sizes

Tall, small
Big, large
Really small
Really tall.

Andrew Granville (9)
Stoke Mandeville Combined School

My Annoying Little Brother

My annoying little brother
Annoys me quite a lot
That's why I'm thinking
Of a very evil plot
I'll wait until midnight
I won't pounce with a knife
Or dagger
I'll pick him up slowly
I'll take him right outside
Then I'll drop him gently
On the doorstep of
Four Privet Drive
I'll run quickly back home
And wait until morning.

Helena Walters (8)
Stoke Mandeville Combined School

The Little Dragon

One little egg rolling down the hillside
Something big and scary came shooting by
Grabbed the little egg and took it down to sea
The creature inside the egg wanted it to leave
Suddenly the tree fell on the monster's head
And then the egg was free, it hatched right there
Out came a little dragon, he was outside
He was so happy but along came a tidal wave
Caused by a shark, washed the dragon away
To get all the way back took July to May
The dragon grew up into a big beast
It will live for a long time, it knows how to feast!

Tyler Sear (9)
Stoke Mandeville Combined School

Mary Mayhem

Mary Mayhem was a horrid little girl,
Who liked to make trouble,
She didn't just make one little problem,
She made two that made double.

One day when she was walking down the road,
She met an ugly, big fat toad,
A boy said it looked much like her,
And that set off the big trigger.

She screamed and shouted,
Yelled and whined,
Till finally when she dined.

She didn't come to dinner that night,
Her mum was worried off her head,
Till finally she went to see her
And found that she was dead!

Now we leave her in peace
Well at least
There's no more trouble
From Mary Mayhem, or is there?

Georgina Hopkins (9)
Stoke Mandeville Combined School

Autumn Days

Autumn leaves fall from the trees
When along came the autumn breeze
Squirrels gather their nuts in haste
To prepare their autumn feast
Rabbits scurry, hop and bound
Because Mr Foxy's hunting now
People gather here and there
To watch the fireworks pop and blare.

Kate Bowman (8)
Stoke Mandeville Combined School

The Circus Poem

Bang, clang, twang
The circus is coming to town
Boom, voom, zoom
I can't wait to see the clown!

Sizzle, pop, bang
Here comes the man-eating fire
Dong, ding, dang
He's someone I really admire

Glide, slide, ride
Watch the trapeze fly through the air
Sail, pail, tail
See how the people stare

Sing, ding, bling
The ringmaster is my friend
Clap, flap, tap
The show has come to an end.

Louise Granville (9)
Stoke Mandeville Combined School

Animals

Birds fly
Seagulls glide

Cats have claws
Dogs have paws

Bulls charge
Giraffes are large

Lions stalk
But I walk.

Farah Chaudhry (9)
Stoke Mandeville Combined School

Black!

What is black?
Black is the colour of ink
Black is the hand on a classroom clock
Black is the colour of school shoes
Black is a sad colour
Black is a mini beast
Black is a dustbin bag
Black is a suit
Black is hair
Black is a button
Black is the colour of space
Black is the colour of a car
Black is a cow
Black is the colour of coal
Black is a colour that everyone knows.

Eleanor Simpson (8)
Stoke Mandeville Combined School

Autumn Leaves

Autumn leaves are all sorts of colours
Brown, red, orange and green

Autumn leaves are crunchy and crumbly
Like when you bite into a Crunchie bar.

Autumn leaves fall from the trees
And change to a leaf skeleton

Autumn leaves are lovely and soft sometimes
And when they fall they're beautiful.

India Rowell (8)
Stoke Mandeville Combined School

Colours

Brown is money
Yellow is honey
Blue is a book
Silver is a hook

White is the door
Orange is the seashore
Green is grass
Gold is brass

Navy is a tin
Bronze is a pin
Pink is a map
Black is a tap

Beige is a pot
Red is a jelly tot
Lilac is a pen
Brown and red is a hen

Lime is a fruit
Purple is a suit
Pink and blue is a room
Dark brown is a broom

Grey is a ruler
That is all the colours I know.

Sophie Theodosiou (9)
Stoke Mandeville Combined School

Little Boy

There once was a boy from Montreal
Who loved to play basketball
For the team he tried out
But if he made it I doubt
For you see he was just three feet tall.

Calum Grainge (9)
Stoke Mandeville Combined School

The Giant's Castle

Way, way high
Up in the sky
Lives a giant
But he is a
Friendly giant!
But when you
Enter his castle
There are bones
Bones of children like you
And there are
Some nice things
Like little beds for children!
You see this giant
Is very greedy
He stands for hours
Staring at all his
Gold!

Rebecca Day (9)
Stoke Mandeville Combined School

The Dragon

The dragon stalks
Leaving footprints of mystery
He has smoky breath
And breathes fire that lights
Up the entire world
His eggs are as big as
Giant diamonds
His roar sounds like a
Whole mountain tumbling over
And he lives for thousands of years.

William Dolder (9)
Stoke Mandeville Combined School

Getting Up

The squeaking of the bed,
The brushing of the toothbrush,
The whistling of the kettle,
The crunching of the cornflakes,
The clothes whizzing past your body,
The bang of the lunch box,
The closing of the door,
The silence of the walkers
And the singing of the school yard.

Dhaamin Clarke (8)
Stoke Mandeville Combined School

School

School, school is not so cool,
It gets so boring,
You end up snoring,
The day is long,
You have to sing songs,
School, school is not so cool.

School, school is not so cool,
You get told off,
Just because you walk off,
School, school is not so cool.

School, school gets so cool,
The trips are fun
And in football, you can run,
Hey! School, school gets
So
Cool!

Matthew Chandler (8)
The Meadows Combined School

There's A Goblin In My Basement

There's a goblin in my basement
Sitting on the floor.

There's a goblin in my basement
Rattling at the door.

There's a goblin in my basement
Talking to himself.

There's a goblin in my basement
Who looks just like an elf.

His wife is sitting next to him
He's drinking cups of tea

His wife is knitting clothes
For her evil family

The old blue wizard's after him
Because he's been so bad

He's been a problem now for years
Since he was a young lad

I think I'll try to catch him now
Before he drives me mad.

Zac Beckles (8)
The Meadows Combined School

The Policeman

The policeman is tall,
He stands by the wall,
His dog is fierce,
He has a brown coat
And black boots.

Richard Nicoll (8)
The Meadows Combined School

The Alien

The alien was ugly,
The alien was bright,
The alien was slimy,
He gave me a fright,
He had six legs,
I chucked some eggs.

James Sidebottom (8)
The Meadows Combined School

There's An Elf In My Room

There's an elf in my room,
He thinks it's a tomb,
I told my mum and she said
He is mystic,
But I said that wasn't realistic.

Joshua Davis (8)
The Meadows Combined School

My Teacher

My teacher plays the piano in a very silly way.
My teacher plays the drum in a very funny way.
My teacher asks if she can blow the whistle when it's play.
My teacher eats roast duck for lunch.
My teacher likes to crunch, crunch, crunch.

Gemma Pryor (8)
The Meadows Combined School

The Weirdest Gran In The World

The weirdest gran in the world is mine,
My gran would dance, but it hurts her spine,
Her teeth stick out when she smiles at me,
She likes fish fingers for her tea,
My sister says she's proud of Gran,
But I know I am her biggest fan!

Sian Kingsman (9)
The Meadows Combined School

My Lovely Teacher

My lovely teacher is so cool,
She's the best teacher in the school.
My lovely teacher is so smart,
She plays football and teaches us art.
My lovely teacher is so sweet,
She plays the drum and keeps the beat.

Alice Walsh (8)
The Meadows Combined School

The Goblin

A goblin comes to me at night,
He wants to give me a real fright.
Every time he comes to me,
I always kick him on the knee!

Matthew Jones (9)
The Meadows Combined School

Dogs And Monkeys

I like dogs with hairy coats,
I like monkeys with furry coats,
I like dogs with their wagging tails,
I like monkeys eating snails,
I like dogs with floppy ears,
I like monkeys with humungous ears,
I like dogs when they scare cats,
I like monkeys chasing rats,
But one thing I don't like is *when they have babies*,
I can't deal with it!

Brandon Ricketts (8)
The Meadows Combined School

My Big Feet

My big feet love a dancing beat,
I'm alright when I'm dancing in the street,
I've got a drum kit so I can play a beat,
But it's hard to keep the rhythm in my feet,
I think my feet are pretty neat!
My big feet love a dancing beat.

Hayley Carson (9)
The Meadows Combined School

A Dragon

A fiery red dragon flies through the silent sky breathing orange flame.
It twists and turns through the empty buildings always following the
voice of beckoning evil.
It reaches its destination and falls through the sky
through the ground being sucked in by Satan's breath.
It lands and sees the fire of Hell, all the people who have committed
terrible crimes are here.
It flies low through a tunnel as hot as the centre of the sun.
It sees Satan working out who next up on Earth he will steal and put in
this molten lava jail.
Next it sees the King of Evil, the Lord of Death, his red body turned
away from the dragon.
His fork-shaped tail matches his symbol of war against good.
His black trident, small bolts of lightning exploding out of it every now
and then.
He turned and smiled at the dragon then said:
'Welcome to the Land of Evil.'

Richard Logan (10)
Thorpe House School

The Blue Ocean

Tropical fish swimming in the waters of the great blue ocean,
The seaweed waving in the strong ocean's currents,
Great pirate ships sailing across to other undiscovered islands,
Coral looking like all the colours of the rainbow,
Dolphins stitching in and out of the calm tropical ocean,
Seals diving under the water like goddesses,
Sharks swimming silently round and round looking for food,
Waves striking up the beach like snakes and fleeing as fast as a
cheetah,
Eels swimming on the ocean bottom as silent as a mouse,
Whirlpool turning round and round sucking anything in its path,
Tidal waves shooting up into the air and crashing down on the city,
The ocean as blue as the sky as warm as a kitten.

Andrew Stephenson (10)
Thorpe House School

The Lonely Sad Dragon

Spurting out of his lips,
Violently shaking from head to hips
Red flames soar into the air
The scaly dragon emits the flare

One clumsy foot stamps on the ground
Five hundred decibels measures its sound
And from the bridge a lone human fell
The vibrations are enough to send him to Hell

The stench from the dragon was ripe and rank
Its sickly smell was musty and mank
Lifting his huge head high
With mournful eyes, he gave a sad sigh

The scary monster shakes his neck to and fro
And his spirits are rock bottom low
Unloved and spurned, alone he stands
Tears from his cheeks drip onto his hands

Ugly and hideous his face and body may be
But inside, he is as human as you or me
Friendly company he desperately craves
Instead he sends men to their early graves

And with one last beat of his wings
He stretches before he springs
Flapping his wings he starts to soar and fly
Before disappearing forever into the night sky.

Jordan Moore (10)
Thorpe House School

It Is A Colourful World

The bloodthirsty dragon watched eagerly over the child
The blue whale diving up from the sea tossing into the air
The venomous green snake slithering to collect his prey
Black is the sign of death coming to you instantly
Silver is like treasure in a treasure chest at the bottom of the sea
The bright gold coin flipping in the air in the blue sky
The white doves spreading peace and serenity over the Earth
The bloody sword slicing through the man's arm
The calm, shiny blue sea glistening in the morning sun
The green goblin lurking in the tall grass
It is a colourful world but some colours are good but some are bad
Nevertheless, without colour wouldn't life be sad?

Aidan Dean (10)
Thorpe House School

The Butterfly

B utterfly flying all day long in its coat of many colours
U tter exquisiteness in flight, fragile wings gliding over the garden
T he delicate proboscis drinking up the sweetest, delicious nectar
T o think this thing of beauty was once a wriggling, green caterpillar
E ating and munching leaves to grow big and fat then becoming
   a dull chrysalis
R ising from its cocoon is when it shows its beauty as a
   stunning butterfly
F luttering from flower to flower cheering even the gloomiest person
L ending a hand to Mother Nature pollinating her creations
Y et after a few short weeks gone . . . but not forgotten!

Oliver Levesley (10)
Thorpe House School

White

White is a cloak spreading peace and purity around the world,
White is a light sending immortality and love,
White is a dove carrying goodness into the darkest corners
of the Earth,
White is frost covering everywhere with a touch of love,
White is snow covering the ground like magic,
White is an angel stopping war,
White is a fairy sending friendship around,
White is the purest gown all lovely and soft,
White is paper sealed with happiness,
White is the sun on a bright cool day,
White is a sandy beach on a treasure island,
White is a wedding dress all sparkling and new,
White is a seagull flying over the textured sea full with life,
White is a tissue shining a bright light around the universe,
White is a gate opening to reveal Heaven,
White is a cloud full with drops of life,
White is a cloth from Heaven sprinkled with the light of God,
White is an albatross gliding over the peaceful waves of
the gleaming ocean.

Alex Saunders (10)
Thorpe House School

Red

A huge devil taking out his anger on the people in Hell,
A chariot of blood speeding through the lava and blood of Hell,
A devil with cells and hearts falling out after the kill,
An army of red ants marching out of the skin of evilness,
The Devil taking the soul out of evil people,
The dragon's fire speeding through, killing the innocent
life of humans,
The fire burning down the goodness of the earth,
The evil hate of the Devil and the goblins,
A dead warrior covered in blood and red maggots,
The poppies of love waving in the cool summer breeze.

William Airey (10)
Thorpe House School

Young Writers - Once Upon A Rhyme Buckinghamshire

Green

Green is the fields of wheat, corn and barley with no man disturbing it.
Green is the woodland glade, peaceful in the cool summer breeze.
Green is the soldier's camouflage while he creeps through
                                    the dark plains.
Green is the swirling and thrashing portal in time, beckoning you.
Green is the misty air around the cliffs, screening your view.
Green is the scales on the fearsome dragon's body, tough
                                    as a diamond.
Green is the spinning hospital ward, doctors peering down on you.
Green is the mischievous goblin, cackling in the cold winter night.
Green is the mossy running track, the athletes warming up.
Green is the mysterious alien thin and slimy.
Green is the drunk sailor's face as he stands at the
                                    deck's soaked rails.
Green is the weeping willow, branches amok, hanging low.
Green is the stormy seas, lashing and ripping at the
                                    defenceless fishing trawlers.

Robert Coates (10)
Thorpe House School

Fast And Furious

The quick, sly cheetah listens for his prey,
With its spotted coat gleaming in the sunlight,
A twitch of a blade of grass is heard,
The cheetah creeps across the long grass,
It sees the quiver of a pair of ears,
The ears are steady as if glued to the air,
The cheetah crouches on the ground,
The ears tremble in the swift glide of the wind,
The cheetah seizes its chance and pounces,
On a poor, defenceless little rabbit.

George Barrett (10)
Thorpe House School

Colours

Black is the fumes of a long endless train,
A witch's cat snooping around the witch's haunted household,
The long and winding dark drainpipes,
White is the clouds drifting gently and slowly through a clear blue sky,
A soft blanket of snow lying on the sleepy earth,
A piece of paper waiting to be drawn on.
Red is a scarlet, vicious, fire-breathing, scaly dragon,
A cardinal red-hot air balloon floating along on a warm summer's day.
Orange is a brave, cunning fox waiting to pounce on its prey,
A beautiful sunset giving a ray of orange sunlight,
A noisy, squeaky firework let off on the Hindu festival, Diwali.
Blue is the sky on a clear sunny day,
The deep sea full of predators and prey.
Yellow is the sun on a bright morning,
A beach ball floating on the blue sea,
Daffodils standing in a line under a large tree.
Green is the long thin grass on a frosty morning,
Trees' leaves falling to the ground in the autumn season.

Neil Chandarana (10)
Thorpe House School

Snowflakes

Snowflakes landing on the ground like hang-gliders onto the Earth.
Snowflakes sprinkled in thousands like icing on a chocolate cake.
Snowflakes flipping and cart-wheeling in the air like acrobats.
Snowflakes diving from the sky like parachutists jumping.
Snowflakes dropped from clouds' arms to the Earth.
Snowflakes, crystals, ever beautiful and fragile.
Snowflakes, blessings from the gods.
Snowflakes, like Jack Frost.
Snowflakes.

Samuel Hickman (10)
Thorpe House School

White

White is the colour of a winter's day, the world is a cake with icing,
White is the colour of the blanket covering the Earth for its long sleep,
White is the colour of the thick smoke coming out of the
                                        dragon's nostrils,
White is the colour of the clammy, cold fog in winter's deep,
White is the colour of an overjoyed bride, so joyful and
                                        happy she cries,
White is the colour of a victorious knight, trotting on his
                                        handsome charger,
White is the colour of a zebra-crossing, getting stamped on every day,
White is the colour of the spoonfuls of cream, being put on a
                                        bowl of strawberries,
White is the colour of a cold, icy ghost, waiting to spook
                                        its next victim,
White is the colour of an unwritten page, the beginning of
                                        a new chapter,
White is the colour of purity of a baby in a Christening gown,
White is the colour and finality of a funeral shroud,
White is the colour of a flag, waving to symbolise surrender
And white is the colour of peace.

Harry Sapsford (11)
Thorpe House School

Black

Black is a hearse carrying a body full of death
Black is a leather jacket being worn by a villain
Black is the stars in space circling the Earth
Black is the sky on a sad night darkening the country
Black is the horse running across the field
Black is the Grim Reaper claiming his next life
Black is the hair on a beard belonging to an old man
Black is the coal burning in my fire
Black are the dominos in a table game
Black is the colour of my shiny shoes.

Thomas Parker (11)
Thorpe House School

The Colours Of The Rainbow

Up in the sky are the beautiful colours of the rainbow
Red filling up the sky with joy and happiness
Orange as the sun glares down on us at different angles
Yellow makes the world look bright and cheerful
Green sends its colour to all of the leafy trees around
Blue, the colour of that brightens the sky to the maximum strength
Indigo gives the colour to every inky word written on paper
Violet uses the power of its colour to light up every purple flower
Is there a pot of gold at the bottom?
No one will ever know
All the colours of the rainbow join up together
To make one big beautiful arch in the sky on our wonderful Earth
And then it just all fades away.

Patrick Lock (11)
Thorpe House School

The Seasons - Haikus

Flowers wet with dew
Snowdrops, daffodils, bluebells
Giving spring its heart

The blazing hot sun
Stands proud in the bright blue sky
Erupting with light

Trees bare of their leaves
Animals hibernating
Soon to be winter

Cold winds blow 'gainst me
Pure white snow descending down
Joy throughout the land.

Olly Speed (10)
Thorpe House School

What Is The Moon?

The moon is like a silver milk bottle cap,
Shining in the night sky.

The moon is a silver button,
On a soft velvet jacket.

The moon is the eye of a giant,
Against a dark face.

The moon is the conductor,
Controlling the tides.

The moon is a silver coin,
In a black leather wallet.

The moon is a baseball,
Zooming out of the stadium.

The moon is a light bulb,
Illuminating the starry sky.

The moon is a searchlight,
Lighting up an area.

Ben Lucas-Lee (9)
Thorpe House School

Skyscrapers

Skyscrapers, the tallest thing on the horizon
Kissing the clouds
Yelling defiance in the face of gravity
Swaying only at a hurricane
Come crashing down when hit by a passenger jet
Raised high into the atmosphere
Appreciated by everyone and very inspiring
People gasping in awe
Elevators racing up and down
Robust structures made out of steel.

Rowan Arkley (9)
Thorpe House School

The Phoenix

A fiery bird, with mystic flame,
Red-hot wings, with golden feathers,
Glowing eyes that can see in the dark,
Scorching breath that can bake steel and stone.

He always wins his far-off duels,
He battles with trolls and knights,
But there is one thing he cannot beat,
A roaring tidal wave, with sharks underneath.

He lives up on a mountain high,
There is only one passage,
Going from depths to peak.
On stratospheric storms,
Where he roams and dies.

If you wish to fight this beast,
Take a barrel of water,
Once you have killed the phoenix,
Spray the water on the egg.

Matthew Booth (9)
Thorpe House School

The Seasons - Haikus

Spring is the best time
For a fresh start and newness
And for joy and fun

Summer - the time of
Warmth and brightening sun to come
August signs the end

Autumn is the reign
Of time to slow down, go slow
And leaves to yellow

Winter, time to sleep
Animals' time to slumber
I play in the snow.

Ben Bridbury (9)
Thorpe House School

Elephant Survival

E lephants, huge, wise beasts roaming across Africa
L olling against trees till they break them down
E lephants, not scared of anything, not even lions
P eople riding these beasts and working with them, but also
H umans are killing them for their tusks!
A lways looking after the other members of the herd
N ever forgetting, down through the generations, the best water holes
T usks which can uproot trees and dig for salts in the earth

S ilently they pass, like grey ships on a sea of green
U nder the brilliant African sky these creatures should roam free
R angers try to keep these gentle giants from harm
V ibrating deep in their tummies they communicate across
                                                    the wide plains
I ntelligent creatures that mourn the loss of a matriarch
V ery close family groups stay together for life
A mbling, never seeming to hurry, they can cover a vast
                                            distance in a day
L eave them in peace and respect their world.

Niall Brogden (9)
Thorpe House School

Snow

Snow is the icing of the world
As sweet as sugar and as smooth as silk

Snow is a white dot
In an otherwise blue sky

Snow is like a carpet of crystals
Glistening in the sun

When it snows it is like a magical world
Created in my back garden.

Thomas Babb (10)
Thorpe House School

The Seasons

S cent of flowers beautifully spreading
P ink cherry blossom covers the ground like a velvety carpet
R ising and falling in the soft breeze
I n the woods bright green shoots appear to clothe the trees
N ight and day the weather grows warmer
G olden daffodils smiling happily in the sun

S unshine splitting through white, fluffy clouds
U nder its hot beams people are happy
M others rub lotion onto struggling children
M eals made by dads on the barbeque
E aten outside as the days get longer
R estless nights children stir in hot beds

A pples shiny on the harvest festival altar
U nder horse chestnut trees conkers wait for boys
T o battle each other in the playground
U nlimited golden crisp leaves falling
M aking a mosaic on the forest floor
N uts being gathering by busy squirrels

W orn out bare trees black against a dull gloomy sky
I ce and frost turn everything white
N ight comes early, playtime is short
T insel is hung to decorate the tree
E vergreens give colour to the winter's day
R ed noses chill in the cold.

Jack Bingham (9)
Thorpe House School

My Christmas Things

My Christmas tree has an angel at the very tippy top,
Sparkling through the day and night.
My Christmas tree is 6 foot 5, so it's very tall
And very wide, my Christmas tree!
My Christmas tree has lots of sparkling lights,
That looks like angels peering through the tinsel-like branches.
My Christmas tree has turtle doves, spiders, grasshoppers
And even bed bugs, my Christmas tree.

My Christmas stocking is long and thin and chubby,
I chose it myself, I wonder why?
My Christmas stocking holds anything you put in it,
So my prezzies grow and grow, my Christmas stocking.
My Christmas stocking is full to bursting
(or so the picture in my mind says),
My Christmas stocking is my favourite thing,
You could fit a cinema in my Christmas stocking!

My precious gloves and scarf and hat
All keep me warm and that's that,
They save me from frostbite, they keep me nice and warm,
They even keep me from freezing in a big snowstorm.
My precious gloves and scarf and hat all keep me warm
And that's that!
They stop me from turning into a human snowman,
They extinguish all signs of horrible coldness.
My precious gloves and scarf and hat all keep me warm
And that's that!

Emilio Iannucci (10)
Thorpe House School

The Aviator

A swallow soaring through the sky,
A sight I've grown used to by and by,
But I still feel a wonderful urge for *me*, *me* to fly.

It started when I was so small,
A biplane I did see
And the pilot he waved and did call,
'Oh come fly with me!'

When older I was interested in Spits and Hurricanes,
But the Sunderland befell my gaze, queen of all the planes.

To the recruiting booth went I,
To ask if Sund'lands I could fly,
For it was a dream have I,
To pilot them gracefully through the sky.

'How old are you?' the off'cer said.
'Eighteen,' was my reply.
'Great, go home, go off to bed,
For tomorrow you will fly!'

A swallow soaring through the sky,
A sight I've grown used to by and by,
But now I don't care about you in the sky,
For *I, I* can fly!

Ralph Higson (10)
Thorpe House School

My Dad's Dream

My dad's dream
Is to have a beautiful boat in the sun

Bobbing up and down
In the calm breeze of the ocean

Watching dolphins
Jumping in and out of the sea

Diving into the sea
Making a big splash like a huge wave

Swimming by coral reefs
Seeing all kinds of wonderful fish

Looking for jellyfish
With long and curly tentacles

Swimming with turtles
Some of them are a hundred years old

Finding a lovely bay
To play on the golden sand

Sitting on the back of the boat
Eating dinner and watching the sun sink in the slight breeze

The sun setting
Underneath the ocean and the ripples moving softly

He always watches out
In case a shark comes along and does some damage

My dad still dreams
But one day, I think he might buy a boat.

Thomas Wait (9)
Thorpe House School

Trouble

Trouble means that you have done something bad.

I am in a stew,
Has someone told? Tell me who!

When you are in trouble, it means that you have hit somebody.
When you are in trouble, it means you have hurt someone's feelings.

Trouble means that you have done something bad.

I am in a stew,
Has someone told? Tell me who!

When you are in trouble, it means you have talked in class when you
were asked not to.
When you are in trouble, it means that you have stolen something from
another person.

Trouble means that you have done something bad.

I am in a stew,
Has someone told? Tell me who!

When you're in trouble, you feel like a steel hard spring,
Something inside me just went ping!
When you are in trouble you feel a tingle going down your spine.
Oh! Why did I talk in line?

Trouble means that you have done something bad.

I am in a stew,
Has someone told? Tell me who!

When you're in trouble, you don't know when to speak,
I feel like a school freak.
When you're in trouble you really are a dead rat.

Trouble means that you have done something bad.

I am in a stew,
Has someone told? Tell me who!

When you're in trouble, you feel ashamed of yourself.
When you walk in the office you feel shy.

Ramir Sandhu (9)
Thorpe House School

The Four Season

Winter
Winter as cold as ice
The chilly wind that blows across your face
The freezing car on Monday mornings
Children waiting for Christmas to come
The wind making the trees sway back and forth
People waiting for the snow to fall

Spring
Spring, the first signs of sunshine
The warm breeze blowing into your face
Young animals hopping around the garden
Birds tweeting in a tree waiting to be fed
Easter has arrived, children go on egg hunts
Families giving and receiving greetings

Summer
Summer is the time to play
To have a barbeque
Have lunch with friends outside
Families with paddling pools, splashing in the sun
Going on holiday to foreign places
Preparations for the next season

Autumn
Autumn, the time to play in the leaves
Families walking in the woods
Cars loaded up with bags filled with garden rubbish
When the wind blows trees sparkle autumnal colours
Everything turning orange and red
And the cycle of the seasons carries on.

James Wright (9)
Thorpe House School

Seasons

Autumn leaves falling off the trees
Ginger, orange, red and green
Children stomping on the crispy mounds
Trees softly blowing in the breeze

Winter frost falling from the sky
Snow storms brewing late at night
Morning sees a blanket of snow
Glistening in the early light

Spring warmth sees the birth of the lambs
A sea of daffodils fills The Meadows Combined School
Birds singing morning and night
Animals from hibernation coming into sight

Summer days hot and sticky
Ice cream melting on children's faces
The sound of splashing water as the children play
The summer season is filled with lots of lazy days.

Marcus Hazelwood (9)
Thorpe House School

My Cats

I have two cats who are black and white
They go out hunting in the middle of the night
Through the cat flap, out they go
No matter what the weather - sun, rain or snow

At home they lie gentle, content and still
When they are out on the hunt they are in for the kill
Their prey is totally unaware
That my cats are fixing them with an evil glare

Creeping through the long grass, climbing up the trees
Springing and leaping, trying to catch bees
Pouncing on their prey, silent and strong
Poor little mice - they won't last long

Asleep by the fire they seem the perfect pet
But look at their muscles in case you forget
These are wild animals, fierce and fine
Two little tigers, I'm pleased they are mine.

Tom Hargreaves (10)
Thorpe House School

Seasons

The rustle of the leaves
The pouring down rain
The bitter cold biting at my toes
Autumn, the time of golds, browns, oranges and yellows

Snowflakes falling from the heavens
Children playing in the snow
Snowballs flying everywhere
Winter, the time when everything is white

New animals being born
Green leaves start growing on the trees
The days grow longer
Spring, the time of pink and white blossom all around

Long lazy days in the warm sun
Down at the beach playing in the sand
Paddling in the sea
Summer, the time of days that go on forever.

Samuel Martin (9)
Thorpe House School

Colours

Red is a strawberry ripe and sweet,
My favourite big baggy jumper,
The double decker buses in London,
Rosy apples delicious and juicy.

Yellow is my Labrador, so cuddly and warm,
Sandy beaches on a hot summer's day,
A bright warming sun,
The ripe banana ready to eat.

Kate Atkins (9)
William Harding Combined School

The Gate

Go and open the gate
Maybe you'll see a plane passing by
Or a splendid garden,
Or an old oak tree.

Go and open the gate,
Maybe you'll see a cat chasing a mouse,
Or a white magic city with white turrets,
Or a castle with a moat.

Go and open the gate,
Maybe you'll see red roses,
Or daffodils in a field,
Or a farmer ploughing his fields.

Go and open the gate,
At least there will be the sweet scent of roses.

Roben Gangaidzo (9)
William Harding Combined School

The Window

Go and look through the window,
Maybe you'll see a cat sitting on the ledge,
Or the trees swaying in the wind,
Or people running by.

Go and look through the window,
Maybe there's a little girl skipping,
Or a car rushing by,
Or dogs playing with cats,

But at least you will let the fresh air in.

Jessica Rose (9)
William Harding Combined School

Go And Look Through The Window

(Based on 'The Door' by Miroslav Holub)

Go and look through the window
Maybe you will see an oak tree or a swampy wood
And a garden of rats
Or a magic city with a blood-red sky

Go and look through the window
Maybe you'll see a dog rummaging for a bone
Maybe you'll see a scary face
Or an Orc eye
Or a picture of a good picture

Go and look through the window
If there's a fog
It will clear

Go and look through the window
If there's only the black darkness
And there's only a bright moon
Or the bristling wind
Even if there's nothing there
Go and look through the window
At least
There'll be a
Draught.

Jordan Richardson (8)
William Harding Combined School

Colours

Blue
Blue is the sea
Or a summer's day sky
Or my dad's new car
Or an eye

Pink
Pink is the pig
Or a rose
Or some people's skin
Or my cat's nose.

Kaimen Hercules (8)
William Harding Combined School

My Dog

Floppy ears like the branches on a willow tree
Dirty paws like a chocolate doughnut
Fat as a lazy cat
Wet nose like a waterfall
Cute as a kitten
His face is as droopy as a bulldog's face
Soft as a bear's furry coat
Silly as a monkey with no brain.

Harri Blake (8)
William Harding Combined School

Dogs

Dogs walk and talk together
Gleam and shine like the beaming sun
When the dogs are running they beat the cheetahs
Even when they have a handicap on

A dog barks with joy when it's out
Never take it to be a toy like an ordinary toy
It has a dark brown coat like chocolate

It's like a teddy how soft it is
Like warm blankets
It reminds me of my friends, my very best friends
Because they're special to me, if I got what I really wanted

It reminds you that you're not the only one living
It wouldn't be the same without it
It's as brave as a fierce knight
It's as good as gold.

Peter Atcheson (8)
William Harding Combined School

Colours

Black is the New Zealand rugby team,
Black is the blackbirds in the night air,
Black is the dog's fur being stroked,
Black are the shoes being polished every day.

Green is the grass where rugby is played,
Green are the eyes of a cat in the light,
Green is the literacy homework book,
Green are the leaves on top of the trees.

Nathan Bilton (9)
William Harding Combined School

The Dog

There is a dog called Fergus,
He howls like a wolf,
He curls up like a ball of wool,
He always sleeps like a sleeping star.

When he wakes up, he growls like a bear,
Fergus is as cuddly as a tiger cub,
But when he goes for a walk, he always goes in mucky fields,
He loves lots of cuddles
And likes cats a lot,
He licks them a lot.

He is as cuddly as a rabbit,
Fergus like to dance,
Fergus growls like a roaring sea,
Fergus is as handsome as a handsome fairytale prince.

Hannah Jackson (8)
William Harding Combined School

Colours

White is snow falling on the ground,
Or the puffy clouds drifting away,
Or the swan swimming gracefully along the river.

Orange is the sun twirling around high in the sky,
Or the clownfish swimming in the ocean,
Or the goldfish with its friends in the bowl.

Gemma Cullen (9)
William Harding Combined School

Go And Open The Curtains

(Based on 'The Door' by Miroslav Holub)

Go and open the curtains,
Look on your window sill,
Look outside at the birds in the sky,
Even a ginger cat out on the path,
Go and open the curtains, take a peep.

Go and open the curtains,
You might see a butterfly,
Or a car moving on the road,
You might see a person putting nuts
In a tree for a thrush or crow.

Go and open the curtains,
You can see the milkman,
Or your garden with a swing or slide,
Don't hesitate, just open them!

At least you can see the sky or sun!

Amy Miller (8)
William Harding Combined School

Colours

Brown is the colour of a snail's shiny shell,
Or a dog panting on the doorstep,
Or a fence with a new coat of paint,
Or the bark of a tall tree.

Red is the colour of roses dancing in the breeze,
Or an apple hanging on a tree,
Or a house of new bricks,
Or lips that have been painted.

Hannah Zealey (9)
William Harding Combined School

The Window
(Based on 'The Door' by Miroslav Holub)

Go and look through the window,
Maybe you'll see a rosy red apple or a green fresh tree,
Or a dog playing with a ball,
Or two birds fighting over a worm.

Go and look through the windows,
Maybe there's a robin sitting on the window ledge,
Or a cat stuck up a tree,
Or two boys playing football.

Go and open the window,
Even if there's only the wind blowing,
Even if there's no one around you,

At least you'll let the cold in!

Tara Eastwood (8)
William Harding Combined School

Purple And Blue Are The Colours For You

Purple is a grape on a vine,
Or an amethyst set into a ring,
Or pansies in a garden,
Or a bruise on my knee.

Blue is the summer sky,
Or the bluebells outside,
Or the sea in the middle of spring,
Or a sapphire set in a crown.

Tegan Pocknell (8)
William Harding Combined School

The Window

Go and open the window,
Maybe you'll see a honey cat peering back at you,
Or a seagull swooping down,
Or a view of a multicoloured sunset.

Go and open the window,
Maybe there's a dog
Splashing in the river,
Or clowns juggling fire,
Or a lion hunting her prey.

Go and open the window,
Even if there's only the
Clatter of a ladder,
Even if there's only
A gentle breeze,
At least there will be a
Reflection of you.

Emily Davitt (9)
William Harding Combined School

Colours Poem

Blue
Blue is the morning day,
Blue is the wavy sea,
Blue is the fresh water trickling down the stream,
Blue is part of my world.

White
White is the snow falling from the sky,
White are the clouds silently whistling by
White is the ice frosting far and wide,
White is the flour mixed in your cake.

Ben Parsons (9)
William Harding Combined School

Colours

Yellow is a shimmering star,
Or a buttercup blowing in the wind,
A fluffy baby chick cheeping,
Or butter melting on hot toast.

Blue is a bluebell growing in the woods,
Or the colour of the sky on a hot summer day,
A blue tit swiftly flying by,
Or clear water flowing down the river.

Orange is the burning blazing fire,
Or a juicy orange squirting in my eye,
The sunset setting after a beautiful day,
Or the beak of a duckling nibbling bread.

Gold is the crown that sparkles on the Queen,
Or five gold rings twinkling on your hand,
A one pound coin that has been stamped at the mint,
Or golden hair waving in the wind.

Sophie Bateman (8)
William Harding Combined School

Colours

Red is the Arsenal shirt being the best at
The top of the scoreboard,
Looking deeply into the burning fire,
A red tomato rolling round the room.

White is a cold windy ball of snow,
White are the bubbles floating from lemonade
And the colour of my dog, Lela's chest,
White is for steam floating in the air.

Bethany Rand (8)
William Harding Combined School

Colours

Red is the colour of the sunshine,
The colour of your nose when you have a bad cold,
The heart pumping in your body,
The colour of your lips when discoing!

Blue is the colour of the sky,
The colour of my eyes,
The sea roaring with big waves,
The lava in my lava lamp!

White is the colour of my teeth,
The snow falling down,
The fluffy white clouds in the sky
And the paper I'm writing on!

Stephanie Purkiss (9)
William Harding Combined School

The Box

(Based on 'The Door' by Miroslav Holub)

Go and open the box,
Maybe you'll see a toy,
Or a star,
Or a fluffy pink bow.

Go and open the box,
Maybe there's a pencil rolling around,
Or a poster,
Or a video.

Even if there's nothing in the box,
At least there is a box.

Haydn Playford (9)
William Harding Combined School

Colours

Green is the meadow in springtime,
Green are the lily pads floating on water,
Green are the leaves on plants in summer,
Green is the mint growing in your garden.

White is the chalk writing on the board,
white is the plain paper on your desk,
White is the snow gleaming in the sun,
White is the polystyrene from a gift.

Orange is an orange sitting in a basket,
Orange is orange juice in a cup,
Orange is a sunset on the horizon.

Black is the cola in your cup,
Black is the night sky,
Black is a witch's cat,
Black is a pop star's car windows.

Kiyana Brigden (9)
William Harding Combined School

Open The Curtains

Go and open the curtains,
Maybe you'll see an ice cream man,
Or a multicoloured butterfly flapping at the window,
Or the milkman singing his favourite song.

Go and open the bright curtains,
Maybe you'll see two boys playing football,
Or two girls skipping,
Or a dog going to fetch his bouncy ball.

At least you will see your reflection
In the shiny window,
Just go and open the curtains.

Rebecca Larkin (8)
William Harding Combined School

Snakes

Snakes are always wet,
I bet.
They slither a lot,
Not.

Once the snake went up
A beanstalk
And started to walk
And talk.

Next day he was so glad,
That he went mad.

Now he's died,
He's fried.

Aisha Hassan (8)
William Harding Combined School

Colours Poem

Black is the colour of a panther stalking,
Black is the colour of the night sky.

Green is the colour of lush grass,
Green is the colour of a frog.

Purple is the colour of an ugly slimy monster,
Purple is the colour of bubblegum sauce.

Red is the colour of your blood when an arrow has hit,
Red is the colour of a rose in the wind.

Richard Searle (9)
William Harding Combined School

Colours

Yellow is the colour of the sun so bright,
Dark blue is the colour of the sky in moonlight,
Green is the colour of the grass so fresh,
Grey is the colour of wire mesh.

Pink is the colour of a sweet-smelling rose,
Brown is the colour of my cat's nose,
Purple is the colour of a juicy plum,
Orange is the colour of my favourite bubblegum.

Black is the colour of my warm, cosy fleece,
Bronze is the colour of two pence piece,
Gold is the colour of a shiny ring,
Silver is the colour of a bell, ding-a-ling.

White is the colour of a ski slope, steep,
Turquoise is the colour of the ocean deep,
Lime is the colour of a fruit so sweet,
Red is the colour of jelly I like to eat.

Ross Smart (9)
William Harding Combined School

Colours

Yellow is the shining sun,
Or a lion in the long grass,
Or a golden eye of a dog,
Or a daffodil swaying elegantly.

Brown is well-worn furniture,
Or a wild rabbit in the meadow,
Or a warm cup of coffee,
To crusty leaves in autumn.

Pink is the cat's little nose,
Or the blush of the pretty girl's cheek,
Or petals of a pink lily,
Or salmon sizzling in the pan.

Blue is the summer sky,
Or the tropical sea,
Or a dolphin diving in and out,
Or forget-me-nots covering the ground.

Orange is a satsuma ready to eat,
Or a crab crawling by fast,
Or a goldfish in a tank,
Or a small carrot ready to cook.

Olivia Pople (8)
William Harding Combined School

My Dog

My dog is like a tiger crouching
On the ground,
Her furry snake-like tail
Goes swishing all around.

Her eyes are like diamonds
In the moonlight,
Of course my little puppy
Won't give you a fright.

Her fur is like corn flowing
In the sun,
Don't worry my pup
We'll have some fun.

Her soft little fur
Feels like silk,
Her cheese grater tongue
Laps the milk.

Her prickly whiskers
Like sharp wire,
We curl up
By the blazing fire.

Emma Bird (9)
William Harding Combined School